PHYSICAL METHODS FOR DETERMINING MOLECULAR GEOMETRY

Selected Topics in Modern Chemistry

SERIES EDITORS

Professor Harry H. Sisler
University of Florida
Gainesville, Florida

Professor Calvin A. VanderWerf
Hope College
Holland, Michigan

BREY—*Physical Methods for Determining Molecular Geometry*
CHELDELIN AND NEWBURGH—*The Chemistry of Some Life Processes*
EYRING AND EYRING—*Modern Chemical Kinetics*
HILDEBRAND—*An Introduction to Molecular Kinetic Theory*
KIEFFER—*The Mole Concept in Chemistry*
MOELLER—*The Chemistry of the Lanthanides*
MORRIS—*Principles of Chemical Equilibrium*
MURMANN—*Inorganic Complex Compounds*
O'DRISCOLL—*The Nature and Chemistry of High Polymers*
OVERMAN—*Basic Concepts of Nuclear Chemistry*
ROCHOW—*Organometallic Chemistry*
RYSCHKEWITSCH—*Chemical Bonding and the Geometry of Molecules*
SISLER—*Chemistry in Non-Aqueous Solvents*
SISLER—*Electronic Structure, Properties, and the Periodic Law*
STRONG AND STRATTON—*Chemical Energy*
VANDERWERF—*Acids, Bases, and the Chemistry of the Covalent Bond*
VOLD AND VOLD—*Colloid Chemistry*

Series Editors' Statement

Professor Wallace S. Brey is not only an outstanding research scientist in the field of nuclear magnetic resonance spectrometry and in the phenomena of solid-gas interfaces, but has through the years earned an enviable reputation as an inspiring and exceptionally lucid instructor in the area of physical chemistry. *Physical Methods for Determining Molecular Geometry* deals with an exciting and thoroughly modern field of chemistry. The excellence of its writing will add new lustre to Professor Brey's already impressive reputation as a chemistry textbook writer. This new addition to Selected Topics in Modern Chemistry will provide a dependable guide for the student who seeks to know the tools which today's chemist uses to unravel the secrets of molecular structure.

Harry H. Sisler
Calvin A. VanderWerf

PHYSICAL METHODS FOR DETERMINING MOLECULAR GEOMETRY

WALLACE S. BREY, JR.

Professor of Chemistry
University of Florida
Gainesville, Florida

New York
REINHOLD PUBLISHING CORPORATION
Chapman & Hall, Ltd., London

Library of Congress Catalog Card Number: 65-24062
Printed in the United States of America

PREFACE

THE THINGS with which a modern chemist needs to be familiar and the tools which he employs in his work are not limited to the beakers, test tubes, and flasks which many people associate with "chemical laboratory." The work of many chemists involves the use of extremely complex instruments for studying and measuring atoms and molecules. The interpretation of the experimental results obtained from these instruments may require mathematical methods of equal complexity.

The first purpose of this book, therefore, is to give to the young person considering scientific work some idea of the challenges presented by the large area of physical chemistry related to the investigation of molecular structure, as well as an indication of the mental skills he must master if he wishes to undertake this type of research.

A college freshman in the second semester of General Chemistry should be able to understand and appreciate most of the material presented here, particularly if he has read the earlier volumes in this series by Ryschkewitsch, on Chemical Bonding, and by Sisler, on Electronic Structure. Those books describe structures of molecules and justify them in terms of principles of bonding; here, I attempt to show how the results on structure are obtained by experiment. The reader of this book should have, in addition to some background in descriptive chemistry, at least an elementary knowledge of the calculus. I believe that it is not too much to expect that colleges and universities provide such knowledge in their first year for all students interested in science.

A second use which may be served by this book is to give the chemist with a wider background who uses data on structure, but has not had the opportunity to learn how it is determined, a better feeling for the complexities of the problems involved in securing structural information and for the accuracy and certainty with which dimensions of molecules can be cited.

It must be pointed out that many things presented here are greatly oversimplified. Experts in physical chemistry or chemical physics may justifiably take exception to some statements which, because of space limitations, have been made without detailed qualification. Only if the specialist will tolerate such simplifications in the initial presentation of his field, however, will the nonspecialist be able to comprehend his work.

Finally, it is a pleasure to express my appreciation for the helpful and critical reading of the manuscript by my wife, Mary Louise, and by Harry H. Sisler, one of the Editors of the series, and for the careful typing of the manuscript by Mrs. Linda Arnold and Miss Susan Binkov.

Gainesville, Florida WALLACE S. BREY, JR.
April, 1965

CONTENTS

chapter one

MOLECULAR GEOMETRY

THE PURPOSE of this book is to enable the reader to learn how chemists and physicists determine the relative positions of atoms in molecules. In trying to achieve this purpose, we will find that the determination of molecular geometry is not always an easy task and that much still remains to be learned about the structure of molecules.

The problem of establishing the geometry of a molecule has two aspects, one qualitative and the other quantitative. The qualitative part is concerned with the general relationships of the positions of atoms to one another; the quantitative results which are sought include the precise distances between atoms and the numerical values of the angles between bonds joining atoms.

To illustrate these statements, let us consider the molecules carbon tetrachloride, with the empirical formula CCl_4, chloroform, which is $CHCl_3$, methylene chloride, CH_2Cl_2, methyl chloride, CH_3Cl, and methane, CH_4. We can deduce some qualitative features of the structures of these molecules from chemical evidence and from experience with other molecules. To begin with, the only atom in this series of molecules which commonly forms bonds with more than one other atom is the carbon atom. Thus we may immediately suppose that each of these molecules has a carbon atom as a central atom, with the other four atoms in some sort of surrounding arrangement. Next, we consider the experimental result that there is only one kind of molecule which can be found with the formula $CHCl_3$. This would indicate that it does not matter which of the chlorine atoms in CCl_4 is replaced by a hydrogen atom; since the four molecules resulting by replacing each of the chlorines in turn are identical, all four of the chlorines must be equivalent to one another. If any of the chlorine atoms had different relationships to the rest of the molecule, the nature of the compound with one nonchlorine atom would depend upon the types of chlorines which happened to remain.

To satisfy this symmetry requirement, there may be postulated a structure which has the four chlorines at the corners of a square with the carbon atom somewhere along the axis passing through the center of the square and perpendicular to the plane defined by the square. In this arrangement, replacement of two of the chlorines by hydrogens could lead to either of two isomers, one of which would be called *cis* (meaning on the same side) and the other *trans* (on opposite sides):

Since only one form of the compound CH_2Cl_2 can be found, this square planar structure is not a reasonable one.

An alternative structure has the four chlorine atoms in a pattern corresponding to the four vertices of a tetrahedron with the carbon atom at the center of the tetrahedron, as shown in Fig. 1-1. This is the only structure in which any one of the positions occupied by an atom bonded to carbon has the same relationship to all three other positions. This is the condition required if one is to obtain only one molecule upon putting a second chlorine at each of the other three positions in turn, with one chlorine already present. Physical

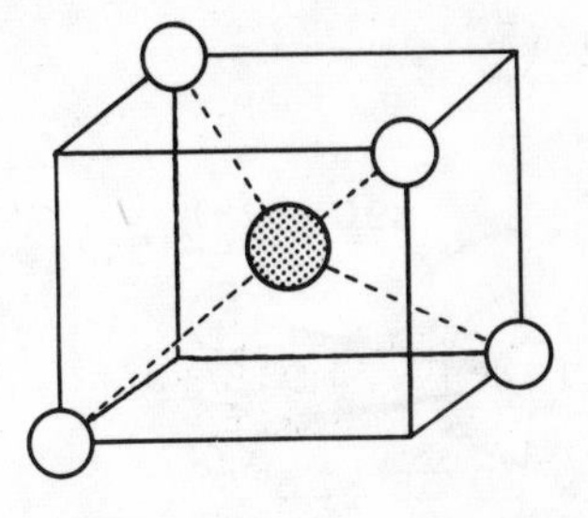

Fig. 1–1. Tetrahedral arrangement of four chlorine atoms about a central carbon atom in carbon tetrachloride.

measurements, of the types to be described later, confirm that this is the correct structure.

By similar arguments, the methane molecule is also found to be a regular tetrahedron. $CHCl_3$, CH_2Cl_2, and CH_3Cl have the four atoms which are attached to the carbon arranged in a pattern very nearly tetrahedral. However, there are also to be answered such quantitative questions as these: (1) In CCl_4, what are the distances from carbon to chlorine? (2) What are the distances from carbon to hydrogen in CH_4? (3) In the three molecules containing both hydrogen and chlorine, are the angles between any two bonds exactly the same as those in the tetrahedral CCl_4 and CH_4 molecules, or does the unsymmetrical substitution modify them somewhat? The answers to these questions require the application of the methods to be described in this book.

As another illustration contrasting somewhat with CCl_4, we may use the molecule sulfur tetrafluoride, SF_4. The chemical knowledge of related compounds and possible substituted derivatives is much more limited than for CCl_4, so that it does not afford much structural evidence. Infrared spectroscopy and nuclear magnetic resonance, however, show that this molecule has two nonequivalent pairs of fluorine atoms. Microwave spectroscopy and electron diffraction confirm this result and give quantitative estimates of the interatomic distances and bond angles, as shown in Fig. 1-2. The reason

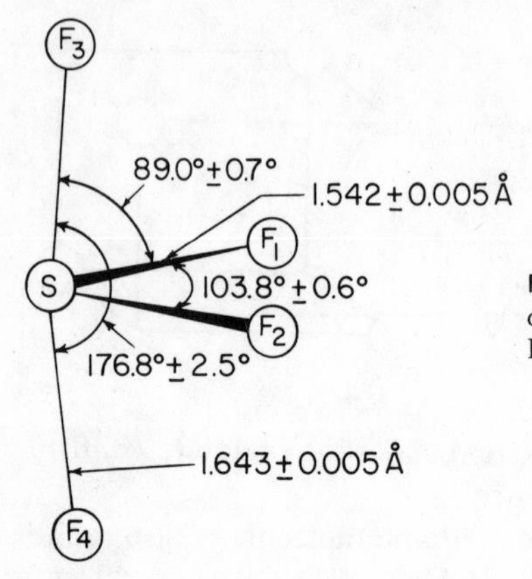

Fig. 1–2. The structure of SF_4. (Redrawn, by permission from K. Kimura and S. H. Bauer, *J. Chem. Phys.*, **39**, 3174 (1963).)

this molecule does not have the high degree of symmetry of CCl_4 is that the sulfur atom has two unshared electrons, which occupy a substantial portion of the space about the central atom.

Emphasis in this book will be on the quantitative part of the problem of molecular structure. However, the qualitative part will also be discussed because (1) in a practical problem the two aspects are often inextricably entangled, (2) the physical principles involved are quite similar, and (3) there have been recent valuable and interesting developments in qualitative tools. The description of qualitative methods can be only quite limited in extent.

chapter two

THE NATURE OF ELECTROMAGNETIC RADIATION

AN UNDERSTANDING of the characteristics of the moving waves which are termed electromagnetic radiation is a most important basis for the study of methods of determining molecular structure. The principal tools for measuring interatomic distances and bond angles depend upon the interaction of this radiation with the atoms or molecules which are being investigated. Historically, the first form of electromagnetic radiation to be investigated was visible light. Since the latter part of the nineteenth century, many other forms have been found, including radio waves, microwaves, infrared radiation, ultraviolet radiation, and x-rays.

The Wave Character of Radiation

All the forms of electromagnetic radiation are alike in certain respects. In the first place, if one measures the velocity with which a beam of any type of this radiation travels in a vacuum, the same numerical value, approximately 3×10^{10} cm/sec, is obtained. This velocity is usually denoted by the symbol c.

If one places a charged particle, such as an electron or an atomic nucleus, at a point past which a beam of radiation is traveling, the particle experiences a fluctuating force. If the radiation is *monochromatic*—that is, if it has only one "color"—the force fluctuates sinusoidally, as represented in Fig. 2-1.

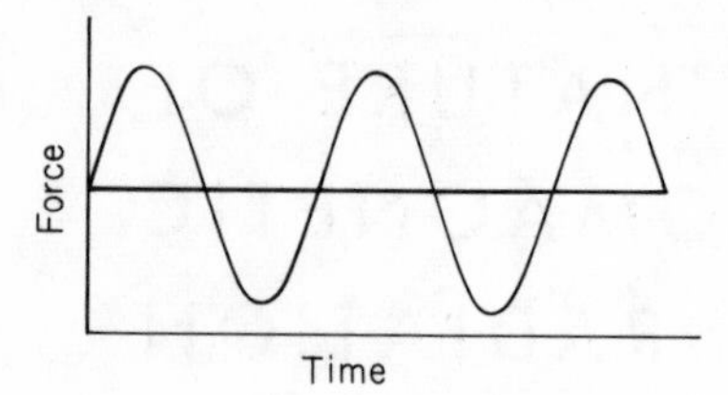

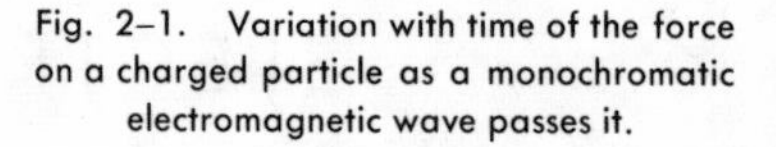

Fig. 2–1. Variation with time of the force on a charged particle as a monochromatic electromagnetic wave passes it.

Indeed, one of the things which happens when radiation passes through a sample of matter is that the electrons and nuclei are set into vibration. Since the strength of an electric field at a point in space equals the force exerted upon a unit charge placed at that point, the second common property of beams of electromagnetic radiation is that each beam includes a fluctuating electrical field. The direction of the field is always perpendicular to the direction in which the beam is traveling. Thus, the force felt by a charged particle is crosswise to the direction in which the ray is moving. Light may therefore be said to be a transverse wave, in contrast to longitudinal sound waves, in which molecules of gas or liquid vibrate in a direction parallel to that in which the sound is propagated, conveying the energy of the sound by bumping into the molecules ahead of them.

The effect of electromagnetic radiation on a charged particle is analogous to the result produced on a cork floating on the surface of water if a stone is dropped into the water a short distance away. As the wave produced by dropping the stone passes by the cork, the cork bobs up and down with the rise and fall of the water surface.

In the 1860's, James Clerk Maxwell developed a mathematical approach to the treatment of light, which is the basis of a portion of our present picture of electromagnetic radiation. Maxwell's equations relate the behavior of radiation to other phenomena of electricity and magnetism. In addition to the fluctuating electric field, they describe a magnetic field which fluctuates synchronously with the electric field in a direction perpendicular both to the direction of travel of the wave and to the direction of the electric field, as shown in Fig. 2-2.

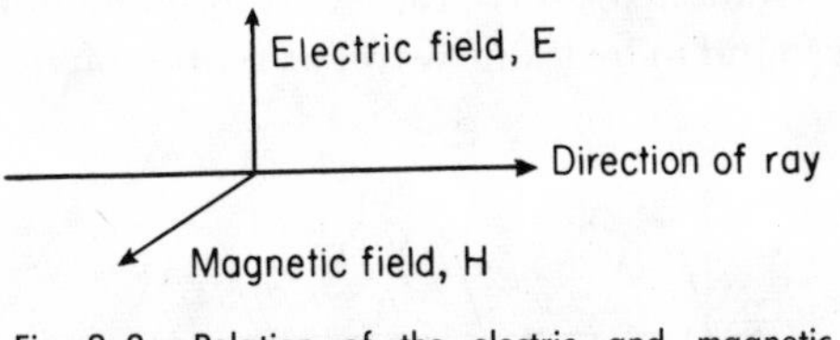

Fig. 2-2. Relation of the electric and magnetic field directions to the direction of propagation of a beam of radiation.

In a beam of light emitted by a typical source, there are components with directions of the electric fields at all possible angles about the beam axis. If this beam is passed through a piece of Polaroid or through a suitably cut crystal of quartz, there is obtained *polarized* radiation, which has the electrical vector in only one plane (Ref. 13, p. 2150).

The Electromagnetic Spectrum

It is now necessary to consider how one specifies numerically the wave properties or "color" of any particular kind of radiation. One designation which may be used for this purpose is the *frequency*, or number of waves passing any point per second, represented by the symbol ν.

As the wave advances, the distance it moves in unit time, or the *velocity*, c, is equal to the number of waves passing any point in that time multiplied by the length of a single wave, which is called the *wavelength* and is represented by the symbol λ. For any form of electromagnetic radiation, the frequency and wavelength are related by the equation:

$$c = \nu\lambda = 3 \times 10^{10} \text{ cm/sec} \quad (2\text{-}1)$$

Thus, the higher the frequency of the radiation, the shorter the wavelength, and, therefore, monochromatic radiation may be satisfactorily described by giving its wavelength in a vacuum.

If one looks at some instant at the form of the electric field of a monochromatic beam of radiation throughout a region of space, it is found to be a sine wave, as represented in Fig. 2-3.

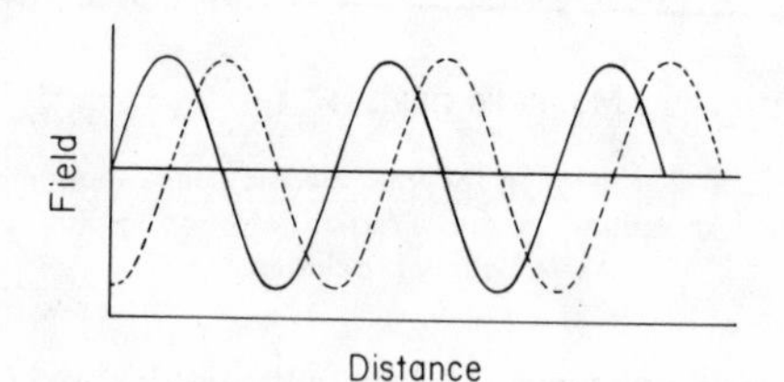

Fig. 2-3. Instantaneous profile of the electric field of a monochromatic ray. Dotted curve shows the same ray a moment later.

The wavelength is the distance corresponding to a complete cycle of the variation of the electric field. The frequency, in such a "snapshot" of the wave form, is equal to the number of wavelengths in a distance of 3×10^{10} cm. This is usually quite a large number; a number which conveys the same information about the radiation but which is much more convenient to handle is the number of waves in one centimeter, called the *wave number*. The wave number is especially convenient in the infrared region of the spectrum, where it ranges from several hundred to several thousand reciprocal centimeters. In Table 2-1 are given approximate ranges for

TABLE 2-1. THE ELECTROMAGNETIC SPECTRUM

Type of Radiation	Wavelength, cm	Wavelength, microns	Wavelength, Å	Frequency, cycles/sec	Wave Number, cm^{-1}
	10^5			3×10^5	10^{-5}
Radio					
	10^1			3×10^9	10^{-1}
Microwaves					
	10^{-1}	1000		3×10^{11}	10^1
Far infrared					
	2×10^{-3}	20	200,000	1.5×10^{13}	5×10^2
Near infrared					
	7.5×10^{-5}	0.75	7500	4×10^{14}	1.3×10^4
Visible					
	4×10^{-5}	0.4	4000	7.5×10^{14}	2.5×10^4
Near ultraviolet					
	2×10^{-5}	0.2	2000	1.5×10^{15}	5×10^4
Vacuum ultraviolet					
	2×10^{-7}		20	1.5×10^{17}	5×10^6
X-rays					
	10^{-9}		0.1	3×10^{19}	10^9
Gamma rays					
	10^{-11}		0.001	3×10^{21}	10^{11}

the wavelengths and frequencies of various kinds of radiation in the electromagnetic spectrum.

The Effect of Matter on Radiation

What happens when electromagnetic radiation travels through matter instead of through empty space? Whatever the nature of the matter, the velocity of the radiation is less than c; how much less depends upon the nature and concentration of the matter as well as upon the frequency of the radiation. The process in which radiation sets into vibration the charged particles making up the matter, which has already been described, is the mechanism by which matter is able to slow down the ray.

When radiation is slowed by matter, either the wavelength or the frequency must change, since the product of the two equals the velocity. It is, in fact, the wavelength which changes, for the frequency must remain constant in order that the wave be continuous. The result is illustrated in Fig. 2-4. Scientists have often found it convenient to use the

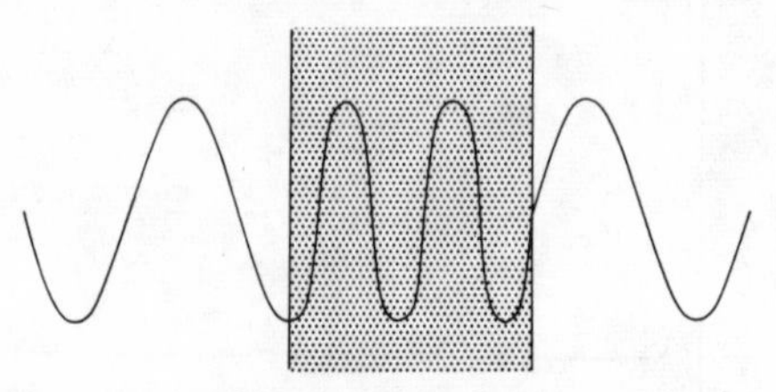

Fig. 2-4. Change in wavelength of radiation as it passes through matter.

wavelength in order to characterize radiation, but the wavelength varies with the material through which the radiation is passing. The frequency, which is invariant, is a more satisfactory quantity to specify.

The ratio of the velocity of radiation in vacuum to the velocity in a particular sample of matter is termed the *index of refraction* of that sample. The phenomenon of refraction is the bending of a ray when it strikes obliquely the surface separating two transparent regions which have different indexes of refraction. If the ray passes into a region of higher refractive index, it bends toward the normal to the surface; if it passes into a region of lower refractive index, it bends away from the normal.

Figure 2-5 illustrates the reason for this. A wave approaching from the direction of region A, which might be

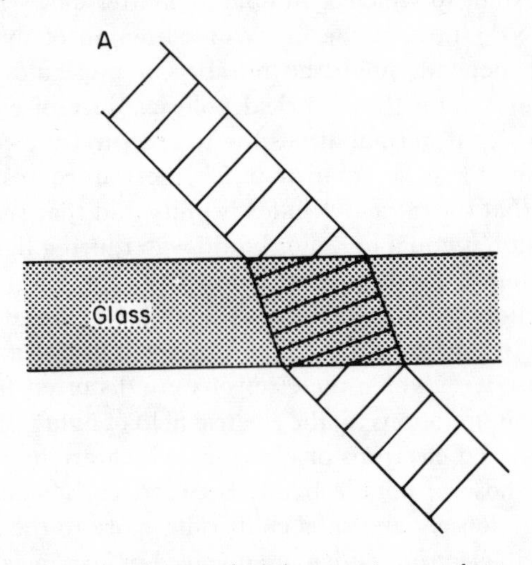

Fig. 2–5. Refraction of a light ray as it passes from air through a piece of glass.

air, is incident obliquely on the surface of a piece of glass. Since its velocity is smaller in glass than in air, the wavelength is shorter in glass. The side of the wave front which reaches the glass first is slowed down sooner than the other side, which travels farther in air, and thus the wave is bent toward a line perpendicular to the surface. When the wave emerges from the glass into air, it bends away from the perpendicular to the surface and thus, provided the two glass surfaces are parallel, its direction of propagation after emergence is parallel to that before entry.

One can imagine as analogous to the entry of light from air into glass, a situation in which a car is driven diagonally across a smooth surface, corresponding to the air region in Fig. 2-5, into a soft shoulder in which traction is poor and progress is slow. If the right wheels of the car enter the soft area first the car will swerve to the right.

The extent to which a sample of matter slows light, and therefore the ratio of the index of refraction of that sample to unity, depends upon the number of molecules per unit volume and upon the electrical polarizability of each molecule. In air, at normal atmospheric pressure, the concentration of matter is so small that for most purposes we may assume that the refractive index is unity and that the velocity of radiation is equal to c. For liquid water, using light from a sodium lamp, the refractive index is about 1.33; for most organic liquids, it is between 1.2 and 1.6; for dense flint glass it may be over 1.9. The polarizability of a molecule is the ease with which the electrons are distorted from their usual orbital motions by the electric field of light. It is found that unshared electrons or electrons which are in π orbitals, such as those of double bonds between carbon atoms, are held more loosely and thus contribute more to the refractive index than electrons which are involved in forming skeletal or sigma bonds between atoms. For example, the refractive index of cyclohexane, a hydrocarbon with no π electrons, is 1.43, and that for benzene, with six π electrons, is 1.50.

When radiation passes through matter, something more drastic than refraction may occur. If the radiation includes a component of frequency suitable to produce a permanent change in the atoms or molecules of the material system, some of the radiation may be absorbed. Indeed, this is one of the important ways in which we shall use the interaction of radiation with matter to learn about the structure of molecules. When a sample absorbs radiation of a given frequency, the material is said to have a spectroscopic absorption band at that frequency.

A spectrophotometer is an instrument which measures the ability of a sample of material to transmit light, infrared or visible or ultraviolet, as this ability varies with the frequency of the light. Such an instrument is shown schematically in Fig. 2-6. Radiation from a source which emits over a wide spectral range is allowed to pass through the material, which, if it is a liquid or gas, is contained in a cell with transparent windows. The transmitted intensity at each frequency is compared with the intensity in the absence of sample. The radiation leaving the cell is allowed to pass through a prism or diffraction grating which permits only a very small range of frequencies to reach the detector at one time. The spec-

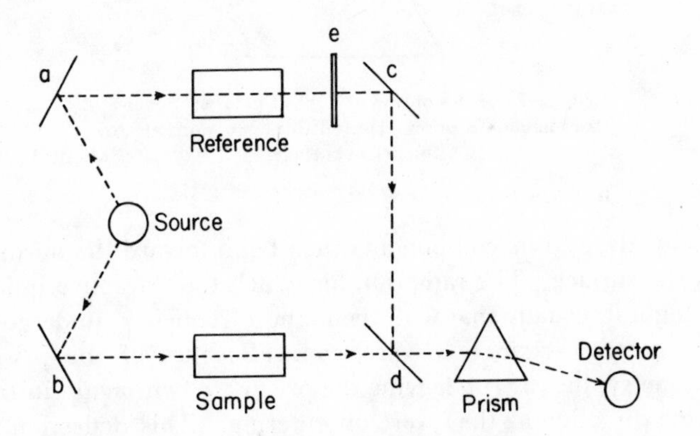

Fig. 2-6. Schematic diagram of a spectrophotometer. Radiation is reflected from the source through the sample and through a reference by mirrors *a* and *b*. The reference beam is attenuated by *e*, which is a wedge that can be moved into and out of the light path, until it is equal in intensity to the sample beam. The two beams are alternately sent to the detector by *d*, which may be a rotating semicircular mirror. A grating is frequently used instead of a prism as a monochromator.

trum is "scanned" by turning the prism or grating so that the frequency is varied, and the operator or a mechanical recorder traces out a curve of transmission against frequency (Ref. 2, ch. 2).

How a Prism Works. One method of separating, or dispersing, a beam of radiation of many frequencies into its component frequencies is by means of a triangular prism. Dispersion by a prism depends upon the variation of the refractive index of the prism material with frequency.

Figure 2-7 shows the path of a beam of light through a prism. The incident beam strikes one face of the prism

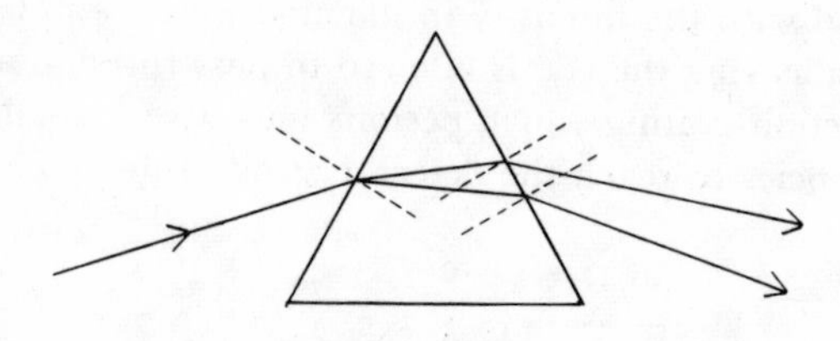

Fig. 2-7. Paths of rays of light of different frequencies through a prism. Dotted lines are normals to the prism surface.

obliquely, and its components then bend toward the normal to the surface. The radiation for which the refractive index is highest, usually that with the highest frequency, undergoes the greatest change in direction. Because of the prism geometry, the rays on leaving the prism are bent again in the same direction as they were on entering. This deflection is away from the normal to the second surface, since the rays are now passing to a region of lower refractive index. If a light beam enters and leaves a piece of glass through parallel faces, as in Fig. 2-5, no dispersion occurs.

The substance of which a prism is made has a substantial variation of refractive index with frequency, and therefore an appreciable dispersing power, only at frequencies in the vicinity of a spectroscopic absorption band. Glass has fairly good dispersing ability in the visible region but absorbs strongly in the infrared. For dispersing infrared radiation in the wavelength range of 2 to 15 microns, sodium chloride prisms made from single crystals of the salt may be used. Sodium chloride has relatively poor dispersive power for wavelengths below 5 microns; at the long-wavelength end, transparency drops as the absorption band beyond 15 microns is approached. If better dispersion between 2 and 7 microns is desired, a prism of calcium fluoride may be used, but this is only sufficiently transparent up to about 9 microns. Potassium bromide may be used from 10 microns up to a cutoff at about 25 microns.

Sources of Radiation

At the long-wavelength end of the spectrum lies the radiofrequency region. The frequencies here are sufficiently low that streams of electrons may be moved back and forth through a metallic conductor under the control of a radio tube, which is the source of oscillations. The conductor acts as an antenna to send out electromagnetic radiation of the same frequency as the alternating current within it.

Microwaves, with wavelengths of the order of millimeters to centimeters, have frequencies too great for the response speed of ordinary electronic circuits. Special vacuum tubes, of which one type is called the klystron, are required. In these, the whole oscillating circuit is within the tube, with a beam of electrons flowing in pulses between electrodes across which a high voltage is applied. The microwave signal may be sent out of the generator through a coaxial cable or in a hollow rectangular tube, called a wave guide, which has conducting walls.

Infrared radiation may be obtained by heating a solid or a gas; it corresponds to the radiation by which thermal energy is transferred between objects at ordinary temperatures, aside from conduction or convection processes. The source in an infrared spectrophotometer is often a Nernst glower, which is a hollow cylinder of refractory oxides, heated by an electric current.

At very high temperatures, heated solids become "red-hot" or "white-hot"; that is, they emit radiation which contains visible light. This radiation extends continuously over a wide range of frequencies, and is produced by motions of atoms and molecules. An example is a tungsten-filament lamp, in which a piece of metallic wire is heated to incandescence to produce radiation rich in visible light.

Visible and ultraviolet radiation is also produced by excitation of electrons in atoms or molecules. In a mercury or neon discharge lamp, for example, the necessary energy is supplied by passing a high-voltage discharge through the gas. To produce ultraviolet radiation of continuous wavelength distribution, an electrical discharge may be passed through hydrogen gas under pressure sufficient to widen the lines of the line spectrum into a continuous spectrum.

X-rays are produced when electrons, given large amounts of kinetic energy by acceleration through a large difference of electrical potential, are allowed to strike atoms in a piece of metal. The bombarding electrons eject electrons from the shells which are close to the nuclei of the metal atoms. Other electrons from high-energy orbitals then fall into the vacant positions, with a corresponding emission of the extra energy as x-rays.

Gamma rays, which may have very high frequencies and wavelengths of a fraction of an angstrom unit, are emitted by nuclei; they serve to carry away some of the energy left over after nuclear rearrangements occur.

Radio-Frequency Circuits and Electron Tubes

It is worthwhile at this point to devote some attention to the behavior of electrical circuits which generate radiation in the radio-frequency region. In direct-current (d.c.) circuits, the only significant characteristic of the path through which the current flows is its resistance. A resistor of metal or carbon usually obeys Ohm's law: the amount of current flowing is equal to the applied voltage divided by the resistance, or

$$I = E/R \tag{2-2}$$

When one deals with currents in radio-frequency or alternating-current (a.c.) circuits, however, there are other parameters of the conducting path which are important, because the observed effects involve the rate of change of the current, as well as its magnitude. In discussing such a circuit, we attempt to break it down into equivalent circuit elements, consisting of *resistance*, *capacitance*, and *inductance*.

Capacitance describes the ability to store electrical charge. Represented by the symbol C, it is equal to the amount of charge stored, q, under the effect of a voltage difference of magnitude E:

$$C = q/E \tag{2-3}$$

A capacitor, or condenser, consists of parallel conducting surfaces, insulated by air or paper or mica from one another. A potential difference applied across the plates by conducting wires causes electrons to leave one plate and move by the conductor to the other plate. Since the plates are relatively close together, the negative electrons attract the positive charges on the opposite surface, and thus it is necessary to expend much less energy in transferring the charges than if the electrons were moved a long distance from counterpart positive charges. A capacitor in a circuit prevents d.c. flow but permits a.c. signals to pass readily, for positive and negative charges can be stored up alternately on the two plates.

Inductance is a measure of the ability to resist a change in current magnitude. The action of an inductor is opposite to that of a capacitor, for the inductor serves as a barrier to a.c. while passing d.c. readily. A solenoid has a high inductance, because a change in current produces a change in the magnetic field associated with any one turn of the wire, which, in turn, induces a voltage in the neighboring turns. This voltage is always induced in such a way as to oppose the change in current; if the current is decreasing, the induced voltage tends to increase it, and vice versa. The magnitude of the induced voltage is equal to the product of the inductance, L, and the rate of current change:

$$E_{\text{induced}} = L\frac{dI}{dt} \tag{2-4}$$

For a circuit containing both inductance and capacitance, there is some a.c. frequency at which the circuit *resonates*. If a current of this frequency is started in the circuit, it tends to continue to flow for quite a time, decreasing only because of the small resistance of the connecting wires. Let us neglect this resistance and consider the circuit shown in Fig. 2-8. Suppose the application of an external voltage initially causes electrons to be moved around the circuit from plate (1) to plate (2) of the condenser in this figure. As negative charge is built up on plate (2) and positive charge on plate (1), the voltage difference across the two plates increases. The flow of electrons then slows down as the voltage difference approaches the applied potential.

As the current approaches zero, the effect of the inductance is to maintain it near zero, and hold the charge on the condenser. Gradually, however, charge begins to move back off the condenser plates and current then flows in the reverse direction. When each plate is again neutral, the current in the reverse direction is a maximum and the inductor tends to keep it at this value. The result is an "overshoot" in the flow of electrons so that they build up a negative charge on plate (1), leaving a positive charge on

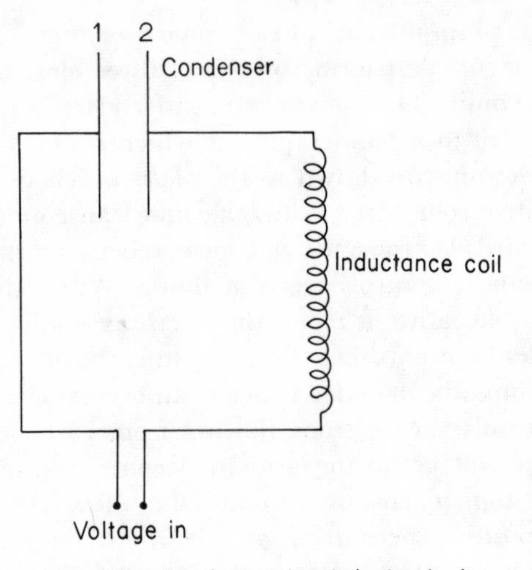

Fig. 2–8. Simple capacitive-inductive circuit.

plate (2). After the voltage buildup at the condenser has slowed down the flow again, the back voltage of the inductor acts to keep the current at a low value, so that the charge stays for a short time on the condenser plates before the electrons start to return. The entire cycle is repeated time after time, with only a small input of energy required to maintain the oscillation.

The magnitudes of the capacitance and inductance in the circuit determine the frequency at which resonance will occur:

$$\nu = \frac{1}{2\pi\sqrt{LC}} \qquad (2\text{-}5)$$

By placing a variable capacitor in a circuit, it is possible to "tune" the circuit, or adjust it to be in resonance at any desired frequency over a considerable range.

Electromagnetic radiation in the wavelength range of meters to thousands of meters is conveniently generated by use of a vacuum tube as an electronic oscillator. A vacuum tube of the simplest form consists of three electrodes in an evacuated bulb. The *cathode*, or negative electrode, is heated by a filament to a temperature at which it emits electrons. These electrons are drawn to the *plate*, which is kept at a high positive voltage, and thus the tube can conduct a current. A third electrode, the *grid*, located between the cathode and the plate, controls electron flow. When the grid is sufficiently negative, it repels the electrons coming from the cathode and prevents them from reaching the plate.

A vacuum tube intended to act as an oscillator is arranged so that a pulse of electrons flowing from cathode to plate causes the voltage on the grid to become negative. After this has stopped current through the tube, the grid can become positive, permitting another pulse of electrons to reach the plate. The cycle is repeated, and the frequency of its repetition is equal to the frequency of the signal which is generated. The frequency is controlled by adjusting the capacitance and inductance of elements in the circuit.

The Superposition Principle and Diffraction

One of the key aspects of the behavior of electromagnetic radiation is the result obtained when two wave trains pass by the same point in space. The principle to be applied here is simply that the resultant electric field at a point at any instant is the algebraic sum of the electric fields contributed at that instant and that point by each of the rays which is passing the point. Thus two wave trains may partially or entirely cancel one another in what is termed destructive interference, provided the electric fields of the waves are directed oppositely to one another. Under other circumstances, two wave trains may reinforce one another, or constructively interfere.

To illustrate superposition of wave trains let us imagine two like sources of monochromatic radiation, placed very close together compared to the wavelength of the emitted beam. If the sources are oscillating in phase with one another, the wave patterns might look as in Fig. 2-9(a). The resultant shown by the heavy line is a wave which has the same frequency but twice the amplitude of that from a single oscillator. If, however, the two sources are oscillating out of phase with one another, that is, one is "up" while the other is "down" and vice versa, the waves add to give a zero resultant, as shown in Fig. 2-9(b).

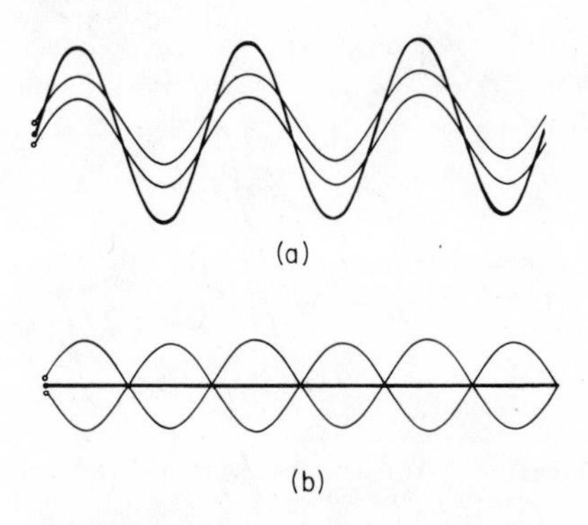

Fig. 2–9. Waves emitted by sources very close together. The resultants are shown as heavy lines. (a) Two waves in phase. (b) Two waves out of phase.

If, now, the two sources are moved a little apart from one another, but kept within a distance comparable to the wavelength of the radiation they are emitting, the interference results depend upon the direction from which the sources are viewed. As the viewer, in a plane which contains the line joining the two sources, traverses a closed path about the sources, he finds alternating regions of high and low intensity. Fig. 2-10 shows two extremes. In (a), the waves coming to the viewer from the sources are in phase with

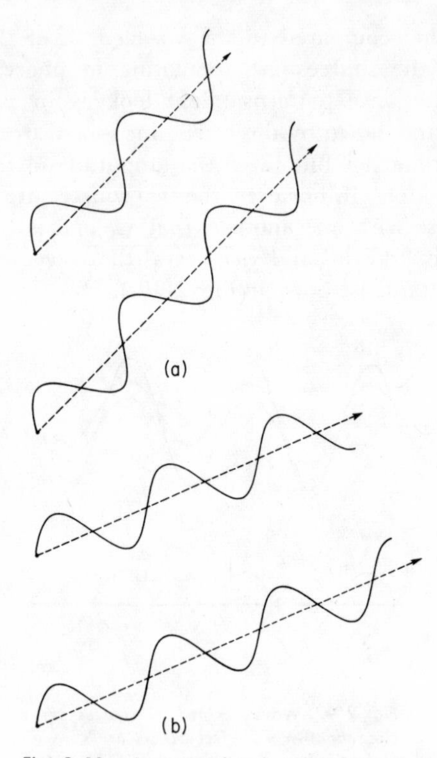

Fig. 2–10. An example showing how the waves emitted by two sources at a distance apart of the order of the wavelength may have a varying resultant intensity, even if the sources are oscillating in phase. (a) Radiation viewed from an angle so that the two waves are in phase. (b) Radiation viewed from an angle at which there is zero resultant intensity.

one another, and constructive interference results; in (b), they are half a wavelength out of phase, so that the resultant intensity is zero.

If one rules on the surface of a piece of glass or plastic a series of parallel straight grooves evenly spaced and very close together, the result is a diffraction grating. If light is transmitted or reflected by this grating, each of the grooves acts as a secondary radiator, and maxima of light intensity are observed at those angles which meet the requirement for constructive interference. This requirement is that the difference in length of path from the viewer to any two of the sources be an integral number of wavelengths, so that the various rays arriving at the viewer's location are in phase

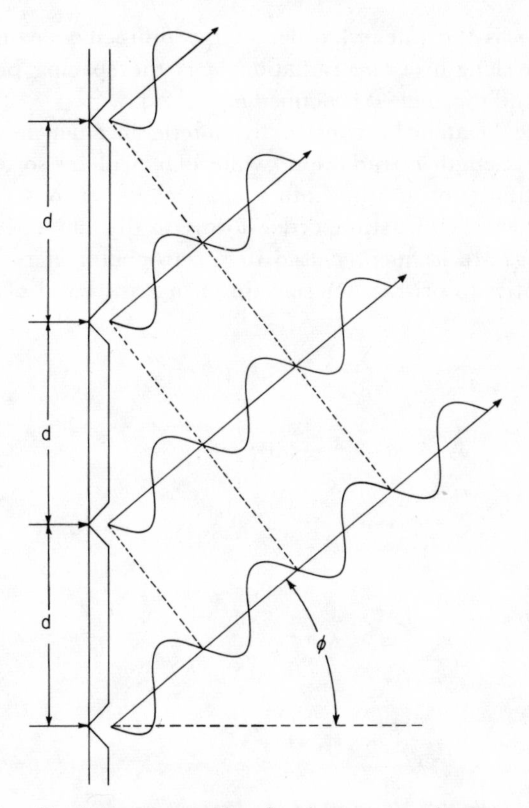

Fig. 2–11. Cross-section of a plane grating, showing first-order diffracted beam.

with one another. The beam for which the path difference for rays from successive scattering lines is one wavelength is called the *first-order* diffracted beam, that for a difference of two wavelengths, the *second-order* beam, and so on. Fig. 2-11 shows the production of the first-order beam for light incident normally on a grating. The intensity maxima appear at angles which satisfy the relationship

$$n\lambda = d \sin \phi \tag{2-6}$$

where n is the integral order of the diffracted beam, λ is the wavelength of the radiation, d is the spacing between lines, and the angle ϕ is defined in Fig. 2-11.

Since the angle for constructive interference depends upon the wavelength of radiation, white light will be sorted out by a diffraction grating into spectra of its various components; each diffraction order forms a distinct spectrum. Gratings are frequently used in spectrophotometers, as an alternative to prisms, for selecting a narrow band of radiation.

chapter three

DIFFRACTION METHODS

AT THE end of the previous chapter, the diffraction of radiation by a pattern ruled on a piece of glass, a diffraction grating, was described. The radiation with which such a grating can be used is in the visible or infrared region of the spectrum, because it is possible, at least with great care, to rule lines at intervals of several thousand angstroms. In similar fashion, nature provides interatomic distances in molecules and in solids which are of the order of magnitude of the wavelengths of x-rays or of the wavelengths associated with electrons traveling with easily attainable velocities. Something more will be said later about the circumstance that an electron is, or has as a part of its nature, a wave of a particular length. The subject of this chapter is the study of patterns of atomic arrangement by interpretation of the diffraction effects observed when x-rays, electrons, or even neutrons, are reflected or transmitted by solid or gaseous samples of matter.

Crystal Structure Determination by X-Ray Methods

Atoms in a solid may act as a three-dimensional array of scattering centers for radiation of appropriate wavelength. We may imagine an x-ray beam, of a few angstroms wavelength, setting into vibration the electrons in the atoms of the solid, which in turn send out radiation of the same frequency in all directions in space. The waves from neighboring atoms interfere with one another, and, if the atoms in the solid have a regular order, a diffraction or interference pattern of alternating high and low intensities results. A photographic plate exposed to a beam of x-rays which has passed through a crystal is shown in Fig. 3-1. The spots on the plate correspond to the directions at which constructive reinforcement of the scattered rays occurs.

Nature of Crystalline Structure. Our problem is to deduce from a diffraction pattern relative atomic positions. We must first, however, understand something about the structure of crystals. In any solid, each atom has a fixed site. Although it may bounce about, the atom cannot leave the compartment in which it is enclosed by its neighbors without changing the nature of the solid.

In a crystalline solid, the structure is regular, in the sense that, if one travels along in any direction through the solid, there is a sequence of atoms which recurs at some regular spacing called the *repeat distance* or the *translation distance.* If an atom is moved from one point in the crystal to another point a distance away equal to some multiple of the repeat distance for the direction in which it is moving, the new location after the movement is indistinguishable in environment from the original location before movement. Thus the entire crystal could be moved, or translated, this distance without changing anything except at the very edges.

Solids have relationships to the atoms which make them up which vary with the way in which the atoms are held together. These relationships are important in determining the structure of a solid, but they do not enter significantly in determining diffraction patterns. To illustrate, the solid may be made by stacking individual atoms, as in a metal, or by packing together positive and negative ions as in most salts, including sodium chloride. It may be an aggregate of neutral molecules, as in carbon dioxide or iodine or most

Fig. 3–1. A Laue photograph of a single crystal of germanium, 0.5 mm thick. This pattern was obtained by a special technique, using 150,000 volt x-rays, which have much greater penetrating power than the usual x-ray beam. (Reproduced by permission from B. Paretzkin and H. S. Peiser, *Science*, **146,** 260 (1964).)

organic solids. In any of these cases, the packing of the units is determined by their size and shape and by the way in which they can fit alongside one another, while preserving the composition of the crystal. Sometimes, in contrast, the solid is one large molecule in two or three dimensions, as with ice or diamond or quartz, and geometry of packing is determined principally by the nature and direction of the covalent bonds which are present. However, the diffraction patterns are determined primarily by the locations of atoms, rather than by the nature of their bonds.

Returning now to the description of atomic locations in the solid, it is convenient to employ the concept of a *unit cell* in specifying the structure of a crystal. The unit cell is the basic building block of the crystal: by placing together many identical unit cells, all oriented in the same way, the entire crystal can be constructed, much in the way a brick wall is built of many identical bricks.

There is often some latitude in the way in which a unit cell is defined. To illustrate, suppose a number of spheres such as marbles, uniform in size, are placed on a plane surface so that they are packed together as closely as possible, as represented in Fig. 3-2. This figure may also be

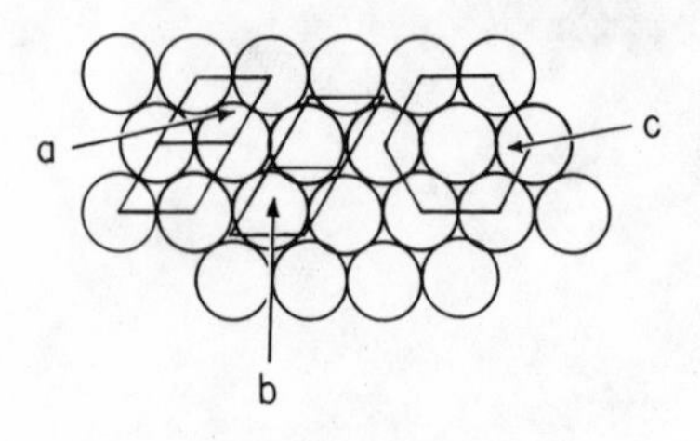

Fig. 3–2. Close packing of uniform spheres on a flat surface, with three ways of choosing the two-dimensional unit cell. Two adjoining unit cells of type *a*, two of type *b*, and one of type *c* are shown.

considered to be a cross section through a three-dimensional atomic crystal structure, and we shall refer to the spheres as atoms. Some ways in which the two-dimensional unit cell may be chosen are shown. Types *a* and *b*, smaller in area than type *c*, are called the primitive cells, and are preferred for some purposes. Unit *c*, however, displays the six-fold symmetry of the pattern: if one chooses any of the atoms as a starting point, there are six directions in the plane along which one may travel away from that atom along a row of other atoms, and all these six directions are indistinguishable from one another.

There is no difference in size or shape between unit cells *a* and *b*; the only distinction is the location of the atoms within the unit cell. In cell *a* the vertices lie at centers of atoms, while in cell *b* the vertices are in "empty space" between atomic spheres. However, for cell *a* one must always remember that only a portion of each of the four atoms which help to make up the cell belongs to the unit. In turn, each of the atoms is shared by four different unit cells, which have a vertex in common at the center of the atomic sphere. Unit cells *a* and *b* contain one atom total each, while unit cell *c* contains the equivalent of three atoms.

Things are more complicated if two kinds of objects are to be packed together. An arrangement of large and small objects might look like the diagram in Fig. 3-3, which can be regarded as a cross section through a crystal of sodium chloride, with large circles representing chloride ions and small circles representing sodium ions. Here the unit cell must contain at least the equivalent of one large and one small particle; the choice labeled *a* in Fig. 3-3 is one possibility

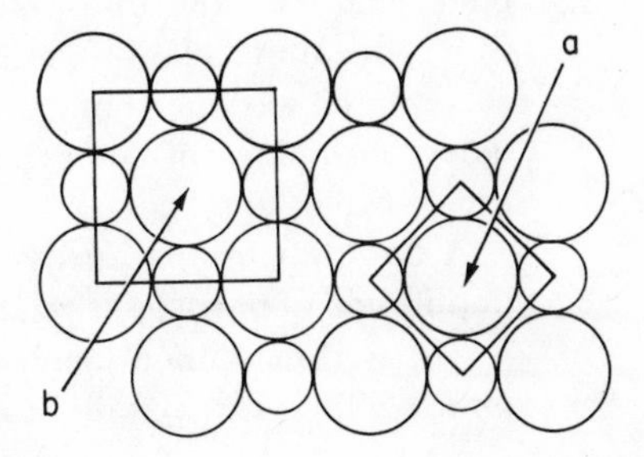

Fig. 3–3. Two-dimensional square array of large and small spheres, with two possible unit cell choices.

meeting this requirement. Choice *b* contains the equivalent of two large and two small particles; it emphasizes the fact that, for this arrangement, both large and small particles are present in a square array.

Two-dimensional unit cells, or cross sections of three-dimensional unit cells, can only be triangles, parallelograms, or hexagons. Objects with five sides, or with seven or more sides, simply can not be placed side by side to fill all space. It should be understood here that the term "fill all space" refers not to the atoms or ions or molecules, for there are interstices between these, but to the abstract concept of the repeating unit in the pattern.

In two dimensions, the processes of moving parallel to the edges of the unit cell for distances equal to the repeat distance generate a *net* of points. The net, for example, might be composed of all the points which fall at the vertices of the unit cells in an array. Then the array itself might be formed by placing the center of an atom at each of the net points. In three dimensions, the net becomes a *lattice* of points, with the points related by translations along the edges of the unit cells.

To describe atomic positions in a crystal, any coordinate system could be used, but it is very convenient to follow the standard conventions: the origin is chosen to be at one vertex of the cell, the axes are taken parallel to the edges of the unit cell, and the unit of measurement along any axis is the edge length of the unit cell in the direction of that axis. Since the unit cell is not necessarily rectangular in cross section, the axes need not be perpendicular to one another. The coordinates of some points in a monoclinic unit cell are shown in Fig. 3-4.

A two-dimensional array contains lines along which the population of particles is relatively great, as shown in Fig. 3-5. In a three-dimensional array, there are corresponding planes which run parallel to layers of units in the crystal

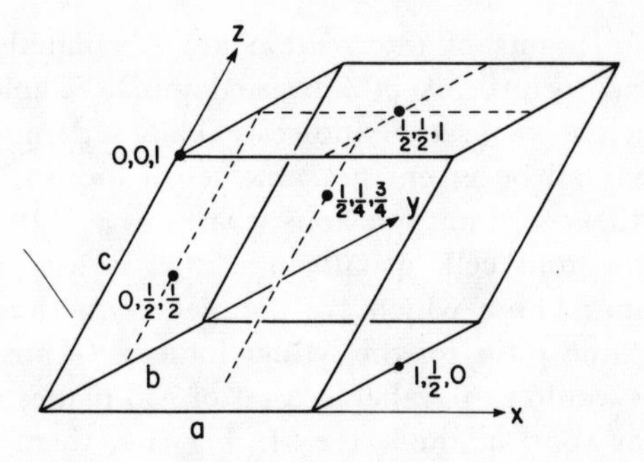

Fig. 3–4. Illustration of how locations in a lattice are described by coordinates which are fractions of the unit cell dimensions, *a*, *b*, and *c*. Dotted lines are added to aid the viewer in visualizing the positions of the points.

lattice. Some of these planes are parallel to the faces of the unit cell, but others are not. The planes containing a high density of atoms are important in the diffraction of x-rays by the crystal.

To refer clearly to crystal planes, we employ *Miller indices*, defined as follows: the distances along each coordinate axis from an arbitrary origin to the points where the axes intersect the plane are measured, the reciprocals of the coordi-

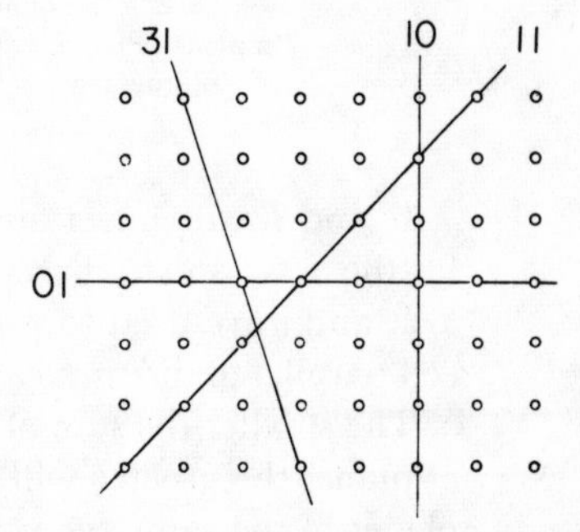

Fig. 3–5. A net of points, showing some lines containing a high population of points. The lines are labeled with two-dimensional Miller indices.

nates of the points of intersection are calculated, and the ratio of the reciprocals is converted into a whole-number ratio, which is the set of indices. Planes parallel to one another may all be given the same set of indices, since the origin of the coordinate system is arbitrary. If the same point in the unit cell, usually a vertex, is used as origin for all planes, those which are parallel to one another will have the same ratios of the Miller indices. Thus a set of 111 planes would be parallel to a set of 333 planes and three times as far apart as the latter. In Fig. 3-6, there are given some designations of planes by Miller indices. The letters

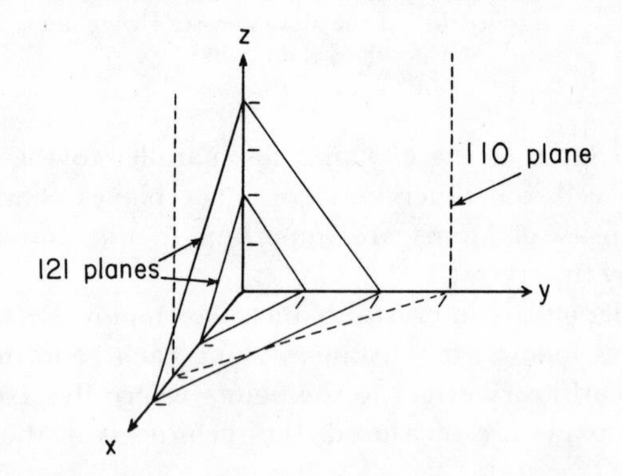

Fig. 3–6. Use of Miller indices to define direction of a plane. Planes are shown by their traces, or lines of intersection, in the *xy*, *xz*, and *yz* planes.

h, *k*, and *l* are conventionally used to represent the indices for the *x*, *y*, and *z* directions, respectively, while the letters *a*, *b*, and *c* are used to represent the edge lengths of the unit cell parallel to the three axes.

The smaller the sum of the squares of the indices of a type of plane, the greater will be the distance between successive planes of the same type, and the greater will be the population per unit area in a plane. For a cubic system, the distance between planes of indices h, k, and l, in terms of the edge length of the unit cell, a, is:

$$d_{hkl} = a/(h^2 + k^2 + l^2)^{1/2} \tag{3-1}$$

The external shape of a single crystal of material bears a close relationship to the shape of the unit cell. Faces of the crystal tend to be parallel to planes of atoms in the crystal lattice. Thus sodium chloride, which has cubic symmetry of the unit cell, usually crystallizes in the form of cubes. However, conditions of growth of a given crystal may tend to remove some of the symmetry elements of the unit cell; despite this, the characteristic angles between faces are preserved in the macroscopic structure. Thus, the use of Miller indices to describe plane faces of crystals originated in the study of external aspects of crystal form, before anything was known with certainty about the internal atomic arrangement (Ref. 8, chs. 1 and 3).

The requirement that unit cells be able to pack together to fill all space limits the possible types of crystals to thirty-two crystal *classes*, which can be grouped into seven crystal *systems*. The cubic system, for example, has the three coordinate axes at right angles to one another, and the unit of distance, the edge length of the unit cell, is the same in all three dimensions. The unit cells of three lattice types representing the cubic system are shown in Fig. 3-7. Additional symmetry characteristics of the lattice as a whole when it is assembled from the unit cells lead to further classification of crystal structures into 230 *space groups* (Ref. 14, p. 127; Ref. 10, p. 40).

An Example of a Simple Crystal Structure. In a crystal of a metallic element or of an ionic compound, the structure is very nearly equivalent to a packing together of spheres in closest possible proximity to one another. If all the spheres are of the same size, as in a metal, there are two ways in

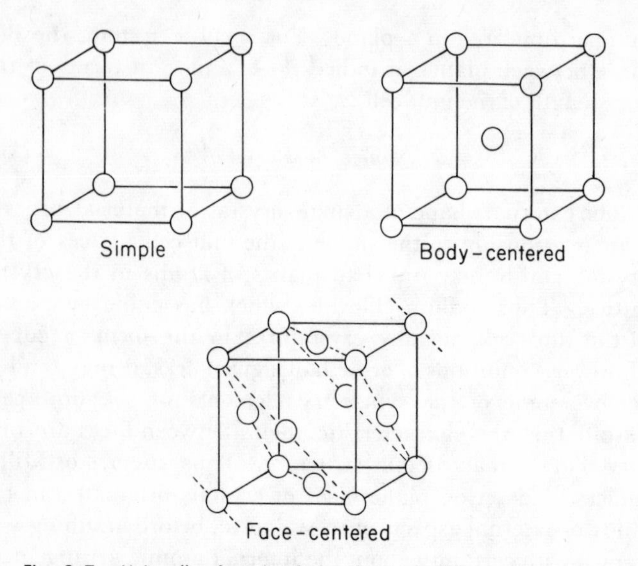

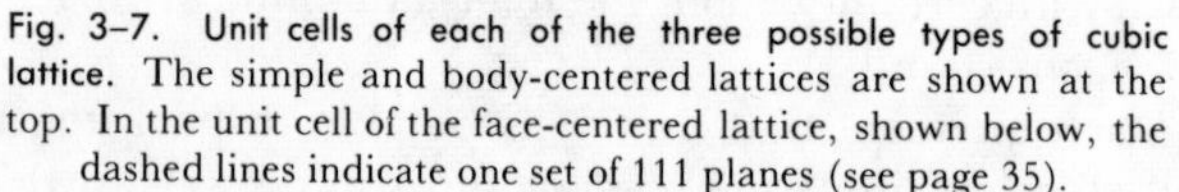
Fig. 3–7. Unit cells of each of the three possible types of cubic lattice. The simple and body-centered lattices are shown at the top. In the unit cell of the face-centered lattice, shown below, the dashed lines indicate one set of 111 planes (see page 35).

which this packing can be achieved. We may begin with one layer of spheres in a plane as in Fig. 3-2. On top of this first layer is placed a second layer, with each unit in a space between three units in the first layer. A third layer is located with each atom again situated in a "triangular" hole between units in the second layer. However, there are two choices in positioning the elements of the third layer: each unit may lie directly above one in the first layer, or each unit may lie above a hole in the first layer. If one continues to add layers, the first pattern, called *hexagonal close packing*, leads to a series of layers in the sequence A,B,A,B, A,B, . . . , while the second arrangement, called *cubic close packing*, corresponds to the sequence A,B,C,A,B,C, ...

We wish now to discuss, in some detail, the cubic closest

packing arrangement. This structure can be seen to be identical with the face-centered cubic lattice in the following way: The layers of atoms mentioned in the description of closest packing above correspond to 111 planes in the cubic crystal lattice. These are planes perpendicular to a cube diagonal, and one set is shown in Fig. 3-7, perpendicular to the cube diagonal running from the lower left front vertex to the upper right rear vertex. One may see, by following this diagonal, that atoms in the first plane, represented here only by the atom at the lower left front vertex, lie in positions which are not matched in the second or third plane but are repeated in the fourth plane, which is represented by the atom at the upper right rear vertex of the cube.

Another feature of interest in this type of lattice is the ratio of the interplanar distances for some of the simpler planes. Examination of the diagram and use of a little geometry enables one to see that the ratio $d_{100} : d_{110} : d_{111}$ is $a : a/2\sqrt{2} : a/\sqrt{3}$. For a simple cubic lattice the corresponding ratio is $a : a/\sqrt{2} : a/\sqrt{3}$. For the body-centered lattice, an extra plane must be inserted between successive 111 planes in the simple cubic structure to include the atom at the center of the unit cell, so that the ratio becomes $a : a/\sqrt{2} : a/2\sqrt{3}$. The differences in ratios such as these enable a distinction to be made between the types of atomic placement for a given external symmetry of the crystal.

The Laue Transmission Method. One experimental arrangement for obtaining an x-ray pattern utilizes a single crystal of the material fixed in position. A beam of x-rays with a distribution of wavelengths, so-called "white" x-rays, passes through the crystal and then strikes a photographic plate. The crystal acts as a three-dimensional diffraction grating, and the angles α, β, and γ, between the direction of a particular diffracted ray and the normals to the surfaces of the unit cells, are given by the equations:

$$h\lambda = d_x \cos \alpha_0 - d_x \cos \alpha \quad (3\text{-}2)$$

$$k\lambda = d_y \cos \beta_0 - d_y \cos \beta \quad (3\text{-}3)$$

$$l\lambda = d_z \cos \gamma_0 - d_z \cos \gamma \quad (3\text{-}4)$$

These equations are the extension of equation 2-6 to three dimensions and to the general situation where the beam is incident on the crystal in a direction having angles α_0, β_0, and γ_0 with the normals to the unit cell faces. The indices h, k, and l are analogous to the order n in equation 2-6; each is an integer equal to the number of wavelengths by which the paths differ for rays scattered by any two successive centers along one of the crystal axes. If the ray is imagined to be reflected by a plane in the crystal, h, k, and l are proportional to the Miller indices of this plane.

The Laue method is not used extensively for quantitative structure determinations, but can be employed for qualitative identification of a crystal or for determination of the three repeat distances. An example of a Laue pattern was seen in Fig. 3-1.

The Bragg Equation. It is very difficult to visualize the physical significance of equations 3-2 to 3-4, and it is a matter of some complexity to assign the spots in a Laue pattern. An alternative way of obtaining a pattern and interpreting the results was devised in 1912 and 1913 by W. H. and W. L. Bragg. The layers of atoms in a crystal are considered to form planes which reflect the x-rays. The reflecting power varies with the number of atoms per unit area of the plane, so that it will be greatest for the planes having low Miller indices, such as 100 or 111 planes.

Figure 3-8 shows a schematic representation of the scattering situation, with the heavy lines representing planes of atoms in the crystal. Let rays a and b be incident upon the surface of the solid at an angle θ from the surface. A detector is placed at the same angle θ to pick up the reflected beam. Rays scattered from each of the series of successive planes spaced at interval d will interfere with one another to produce a diffraction pattern. Consider, in the diagram, the inter-

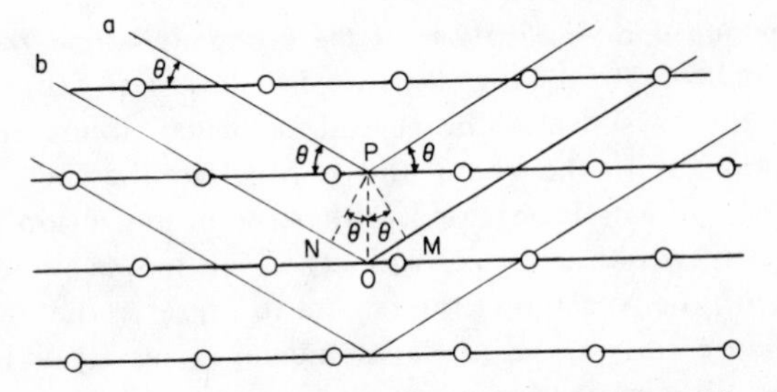

Fig. 3–8. Diagram illustrating the Bragg condition for maximum intensity in diffraction of x-rays by a crystal.

ference of ray a with ray b. Ray b has to travel farther than ray a by a distance equal to N–O plus O–M. The lines P–N and P–M have been constructed in the diagram perpendicular to the direction of the rays, in order to define this extra path length. The distance O–P is equal to d. By simple trigonometry, the distances N–O and O–M are equal to $d \sin \theta$, so that ray b must travel farther than ray a by $2d \sin \theta$. Ray b will be in phase with ray a, that is, peak will match peak and valley will match valley, if the path difference is equal to an integral number of wavelengths. This leads to the condition of maximum intensity, derived by Bragg:

$$n\lambda = 2d \sin \theta \tag{3-5}$$

As in diffraction by a grating, n is an integer, equal to the number of wavelengths by which paths differ and also to the *order* of the diffracted beam.

A well-defined x-ray diffraction pattern can only be obtained if the regions of crystalline structure in a solid sample exceed a minimum size, so that the process of interference is repeated many times. Several hundred layers of perfectly or nearly perfectly arranged atoms may be required to give sharp features in the diffraction pattern. Smaller crystallites, containing perhaps ten to a hundred layers, give patterns, but the spots or lines are broad and diffuse.

Technique and Applications of the Bragg Reflection Method. A monochromatic beam of x-rays is allowed to fall on one face of the crystal and the crystal is turned about an axis perpendicular to the beam and parallel to the face. The reflected intensity is observed, either by an ionization detector (a Geiger tube or its equivalent) which moves simultaneously with the rotation of the crystal to preserve the angle of reflection equal to the angle of incidence, or by a photographic film arranged to cover the range of reflection angles. At the particular angles at which equation 3-5 is satisfied, there will appear an "x-ray diffraction line," either a deflection of the pen of a recorder or a darkened line on a photographic film.

Usually, as the angle θ is varied during the examination of one face of a crystal, several maxima are seen, corresponding to increasing values of the integer n, with the intensity decreasing as the angle increases. For these lines the values of $\sin \theta$ will be in an integral ratio 1:2:3:4 and so on. If the wavelength of the x-rays used is known, there can be calculated the repeat distance, d, in the direction perpendicular to the crystal face. As an example, the 110 reflections of a cubic crystal containing molecules of chlorodifluoromethane ($CClF_2H$) in a framework of water something like ice, are shown in Fig. 3-9. The pattern was obtained with copper K radiation of 1.539 Å wavelength. For the three

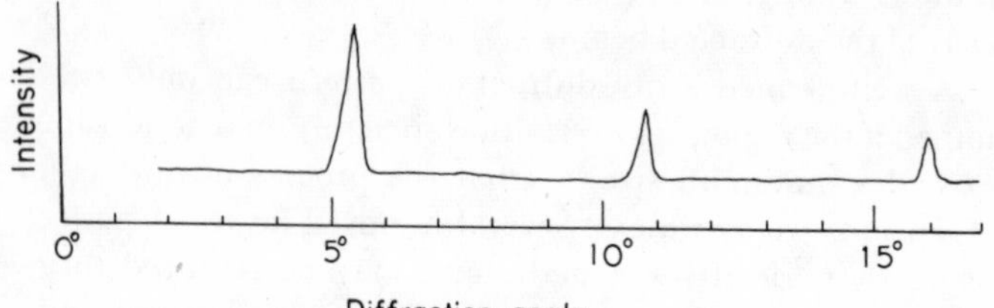

Fig. 3-9. X-ray diffraction lines from the 110 planes of the hydrate of chlorodifluoromethane.

peaks which are shown, the sines of the angles are 0.0909, 0.1822, and 0.2731, respectively. If we divide each of these numbers by the order, n, of the reflection, we obtain for $\sin \theta/n$ the values 0.0909, 0.0911, and 0.0910, respectively. Using the average value, 0.0910, in the Bragg equation leads to 16.92 Å for d_{110}. Since this is half the diagonal of the face, the edge of the unit cube can be shown to be 11.97 Å.

The crystal of sodium chloride illustrates a number of features encountered in structures having several kinds of atoms present. It is represented in Fig. 3-10 and may be described

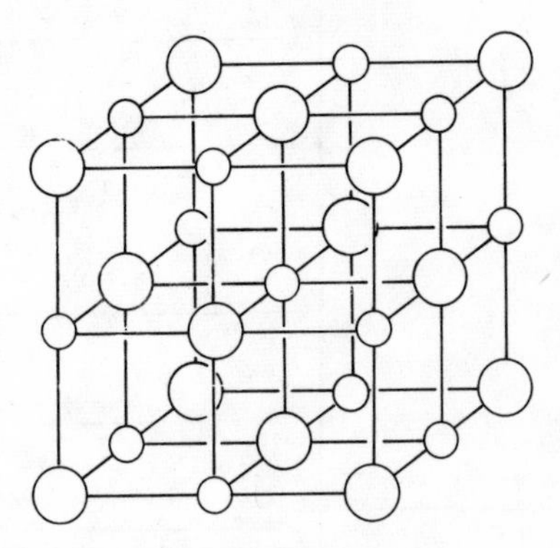

Fig. 3–10. Unit cell of the sodium chloride type of lattice.

as consisting of two interpenetrating face-centered arrays, one of sodium ions and the other of chloride ions. Thus it has face-centered symmetry.

From another viewpoint, it may be regarded as derived from a simple cubic lattice with a repeat distance which is one-half that of the face-centered lattice; if the sodium ions had the same scattering power as the chloride ions and the two were therefore indistinguishable to x-rays, the structure would appear to be simple cubic. The diffraction pattern, however, fits neither simple cubic nor face-centered cubic; it will be discussed in relation to the face-centered cubic pattern.

Consider the 100 planes of the NaCl lattice, parallel to the faces of the unit cell. These recur at intervals of $a/2$, just as in the ordinary face-centered cube. Each plane contains equal numbers of sodium ions and of chloride ions. The NaCl 100 reflections, shown in Fig. 3-11, decrease in in-

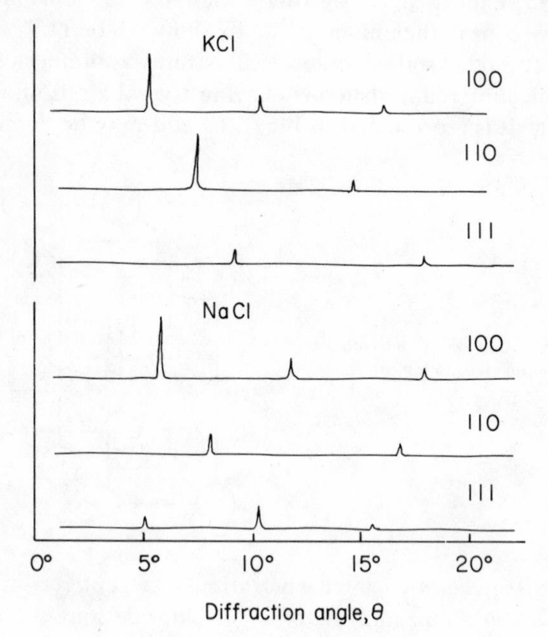

Fig. 3-11. Bragg x-ray diffraction patterns for prominent planes of potassium chloride and sodium chloride.

tensity with increasing angle, which corresponds to increasing order, just as expected for a face-centered lattice. Likewise the 110 planes, which pass through two diagonally opposite edges of the unit cube, recur as in the ordinary face-centered lattice at intervals equal to one quarter of the length of the face diagonal, or $a/2\sqrt{2}$.

The interval between 111 planes in the NaCl lattice is, on the other hand, only one half that in the ordinary face-centered lattice. From the Bragg equation, halving the repeat distance doubles the value of sin θ at which the first reflection appears. Contrary to this, the first 111 reflection appears in just the place we expect for a face-centered lattice, although it is very much weaker than expected. Indeed, the true repeat distance in this direction *is* twice the distance between successive planes, because successive planes are unlike, one consisting entirely of sodium ions and the next, entirely of chloride ions.

The lattice of potassium chloride is similar to that of sodium chloride, except that a is 6.2929 Å, compared to 5.6406 Å for NaCl. However, the KCl diffraction pattern is that of a *simple cubic lattice*, since the values of sin θ for the first order reflections are in the ratio appropriate to that lattice and the intensities decrease regularly with increasing order. This perhaps surprising result is a consequence of the fact that a potassium ion has 18 electrons and a chloride ion also has 18 electrons, so that x-rays can not distinguish between them. Thus to the x-ray beam, a KCl lattice like that of Fig. 3-10 appears to be simple cubic with the edge length of the unit cell equal to 3.1465 Å.

Sodium chloride 111 planes are shown in cross section in Fig. 3-12. Planes of sodium ions are interspersed halfway between planes containing chloride ions. Whenever this happens, the diffraction lines of *odd* order are weak or missing. For one of these lines, the path difference for reflections from successive like planes is one, three, five, . . . wavelengths. The path difference between reflection from one of these planes and from one of the interleaved planes is one-half of this value, or 1/2, 3/2, 5/2, . . . wavelengths. The reflection from the interleaved plane of sodium ions will thus be one-half wavelength out of phase with the reflection from the chloride planes and will produce a maximum reduction in

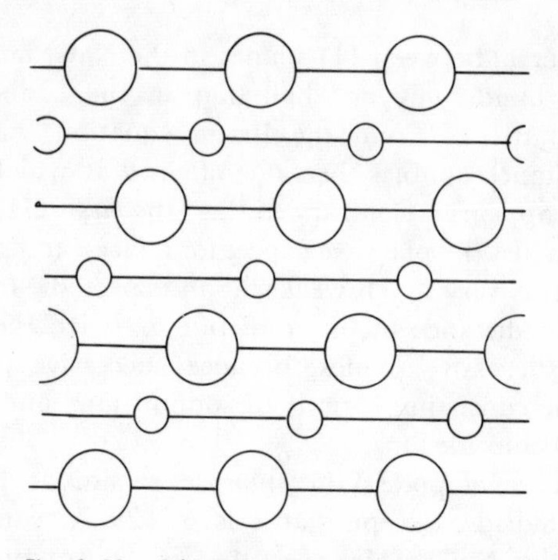

Fig. 3–12. Schematic representation of atomic placement in successive 111 planes in the sodium chloride lattice.

intensity. The even order reflections are of normal intensity, for half an even number is still an integer; reflections from the interleaved planes are therefore an integral number of wavelengths ahead of or behind those from the other planes, and reinforcement occurs.

Another type of lattice which may be used as an illustration is that found in many compounds having the empirical formula AX_2 and called the fluorite lattice, for its structure was first worked out by the Braggs for calcium fluoride. It is assumed by some oxides such as thorium oxide. The atoms represented by A—calcium and thorium in the examples mentioned—are arranged in a face-centered array, while the atoms represented by X are in a simple cubic arrangement, interpenetrating the A array. A unit cell is shown in Fig. 3-13.

This unit cell may be imagined to be divided into eight equal subcubes. At the center of each of these is located one of the X atoms. Each of the X atoms is surrounded by

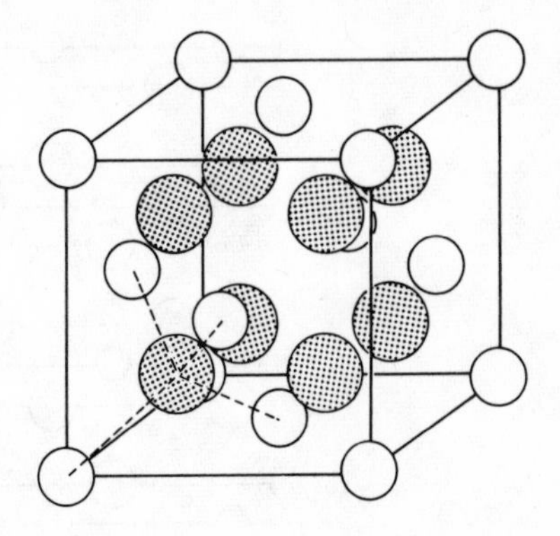

Fig. 3–13. The unit cell of the fluorite lattice type. As shown for one of the fluoride ions, each fluoride is surrounded tetrahedrally by four smaller calcium ions. Although the relative sizes of the circles are approximately proportional to the ionic sizes for Ca^{2+} and F^{-}, they are not drawn to scale in relation to the size of the unit cell, so that we may "see" into the interior of the unit cell.

four of the A atoms arranged in a pattern equivalent to the vertices of a tetrahedron. Each of the A atoms is surrounded by eight X atoms at positions equivalent to the vertices of an octahedron. The 100 planes show a repeat distance equal to one half the edge length. Since successive 100 planes contain atoms of different types, the even order reflections are weak. Successive 110 planes are alike, at a spacing equal to one quarter of the face diagonal, and the intensities fall off normally. The sequence of 111 planes is shown in Fig. 3-14; between two successive planes containing metal atoms there are two planes containing oxygen atoms located at 1/4 and 3/4 of the distance between the metal 111 planes. Maximum decrease in intensity is now found for the second order reflection, since one quarter of two wavelengths difference in path is one-half wavelength, which makes the two reflections exactly out of phase.

The Powder Method. Frequently it is not possible to obtain a crystal of a substance under study which is large enough to handle for the single crystal method. The sample may then be ground to a fine powder, which is placed in a glass capillary tube mounted on the axis of a cylindrical camera. Photographic film is placed around the inside of the cylindrical surface of the camera and x-rays are admitted through a

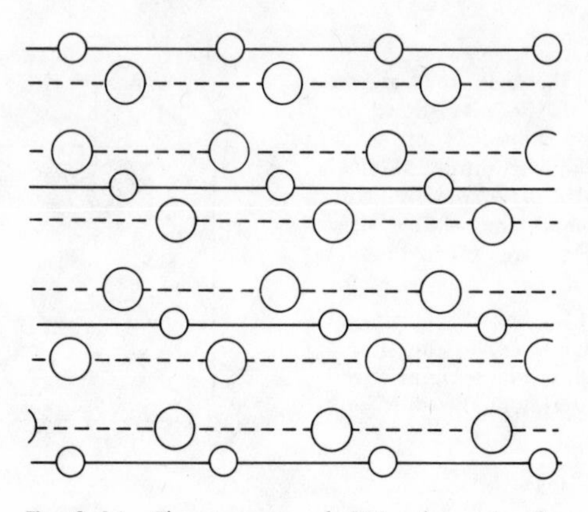

Fig. 3–14. The sequence of 111 planes in the fluorite lattice. The relative distances between successive planes and the relative populations of the planes are correctly shown; the placement on each plane is, however, arbitrary. Every vertical row of atoms does correspond to a row of atoms occurring in the crystal in a line perpendicular to the set of 111 planes.

window in the camera and a hole in the film. Alternatively, the powder may be spread in a shallow flat holder, and the sample and detector moved through various diffraction angles as in the Bragg single crystal method.

In either of these procedures, monochromatic x-rays are used and the diffraction intensity is determined as a function of Bragg angle θ. The powdered sample contains crystallites oriented randomly at all possible angles, so that there will be some of the crystal faces at the appropriate angles for diffraction at each value which satisfies the Bragg equation. To insure that this is so, the powder must, of course, be very fine.

The powder pattern has the disadvantage that one can not assign each of the various reflections directly to a known crystal face. Thus if the structure is totally unknown, a powder pattern may not give much useful information. However, it is quite satisfactory for showing that an unknown crystal is identical with a known material and for determining the dimensions of the unit cell.

As an example to illustrate the interpretation of a powder pattern, consider the lines of cubic gold which are listed in Table 3-1. The first problem is the assignment of the correct

Table 3-1. Powder X-ray Lines of Gold (λ = 1.539 Å)

θ, degrees	Intensity	Indices, hkl	Σh^2
19.07	Strong	111	3
22.17	Medium	200	4
32.25	Medium	220	8
38.73	Strong	113	11
40.80	Weak	222	12
49.00	Weak	400	16
55.35	Medium	133	19
57.58	Medium	240	20
67.70	Medium	224	24
78.02	Strong	115, 333	27

indices to the reflections. Small-angle lines have low indices, but it is not possible to know in advance, for instance, what indices belong to the first observed line. This first line may be successively assigned various integral values which could correspond to the sum of the squares of the indices, symbolized as Σh^2. If this line belongs to the 100 planes, the sum would be 1, for 110 planes, it would be 2, for 200 planes, 4, for 210 planes, 5, and so on. For a given assumption of the sum for the first line, the edge length of the unit cell, a, may be calculated by combining equations 3-1 and 3-5:

$$a = \sqrt{h^2 + k^2 + l^2}\,\frac{\lambda}{2 \sin \theta} \qquad (3\text{-}7)$$

In setting up this equation, n has been set equal to unity; in effect, the order has been incorporated in the indices. Thus the 2nd order 100 reflection is the same thing as the

200 reflection. This procedure helps to keep all the values from a given material on a consistent basis, even when the structure is not yet known.

When a has thus been calculated from the first line, it is then used to calculate Σh^2 for the other lines. If the result is an integer for each line, this indicates that the correct value of a has been found. For gold, the first line turns out to be the 111 line, with $\Sigma h^2 = 3$, and a, obtained from careful work with more significant figures than shown in the table, is 4.0786 Å.

From the value of a and the density of metallic gold, it is possible to determine how many atoms there are in a unit cell:

$$n\ \frac{\text{atoms}}{\text{cell}} = \frac{6.023 \times 10^{23}\ \text{atoms}}{196.97\ \text{grams}} \times (4.0786 \times 10^{-8})^3\ \frac{\text{cm}^3}{\text{cell}} \times 19.30\ \frac{\text{grams}}{\text{cm}^3} = 4.00 \quad (3\text{-}8)$$

Further information about the gold lattice can now be obtained by inspection of the indices of the observed lines. Not all reflections appear; there are missing such reflections as 100, 110, 211, 221, 300, and 321. The absent reflections are often called *extinctions* and are characteristic of the lattice. For gold, we notice that the indices for any reflection are either all even or all odd; combinations which violate this rule are missing. This rule is characteristic of a unit cell which is centered on all the faces. Thus gold is one of the many metals which crystallize in the face-centered cubic lattice described earlier in this chapter. A body-centered lattice can be identified by the requirement that, for it, the sum of the indices must be an even number if a reflection is to be observed.

As an exercise to determine whether he can visualize the geometry of the gold lattice, the reader should show that the apparent radius of a gold atom is 1.44 Å.

One may now be able to see how, in principle, data for angles and intensities of various diffraction lines may be combined to give a picture of atomic locations in a crystal. For more complicated crystals, the detailed application of the method becomes very cumbersome. Systematic approaches which have been developed involve quantitative consideration of intensity as well as reference to tables describing the rules governing the diffraction behavior of various space groups, but these procedures are, in essence, extensions of the ideas that have already been presented. Some of these methods will be described in a very elementary way in the next section.

Complete Structure Determination. A problem frequently encountered is the determination of the relative positions in a solid of the component atoms in a molecule ranging in size from a few to several hundred atoms. Each unit cell may contain one, two, or perhaps four or more complete molecules. Within the individual molecules, the relative atomic positions are nearly the same as if the molecule were in the gas phase, while the shape of the molecules determines the way in which they are packed in the solid.

The x-ray crystallographer may start with full knowledge of the molecular formula and be concerned with measuring interatomic distances. Or, he may undertake to determine the structural formula of a compound of which only the empirical composition is known. Most problems lie somewhere between these extremes, but the difficulty of the solution increases with the size of the molecules and decreases with increasing knowledge of the molecular structure.

The usual procedures involve rotation of a single crystal about one of its principal axes. The incident monochromatic x-rays are reflected to a cylindrical photographic film surrounding the crystal, yielding, in one exposure, a pattern consisting of rows of diffraction spots symmetrically above and below the plane perpendicular to the axis of rotation and

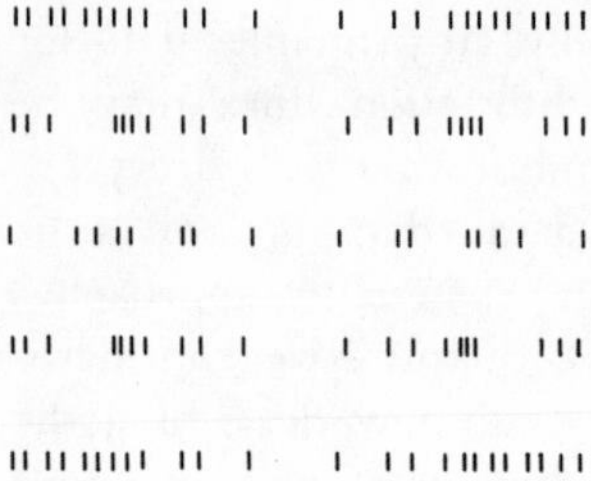

Fig. 3–15. Diagrammatic representation of a crystal rotation photograph. The horizontal rows are called "layer lines." The middle line is produced by planes with indices $hk0$, those just above and below the middle by $hk1$ planes, and the second lines by $hk2$ planes.

containing the x-ray beam. An example is shown in Fig. 3-15. From the wavelength of the x-rays and the camera geometry, it is possible to index the various spots. Various exposures, as needed for the substance, are taken with different axes of crystal rotation.

The data required for the determination include the relative intensities of as many of the diffraction spots as possible. The intensity is estimated visually, and spots common to several photographs are used to bring the intensities to a common scale.

The crystal symmetry type is first determined, utilizing external appearance of the crystal and an examination of systematic extinctions. As an aid in assigning symmetry, the rotation method may be modified to one in which the crystal is oscillated back and forth through a limited angle of 10 to 20 degrees. When the crystal rotates completely around its axis, the pattern is automatically symmetrical above and below the equatorial plane, because each plane in the crystal reflects twice: if the x-ray beam strikes it obliquely at one place and is reflected upward, it will again strike the plane 180° later and be reflected downward by the same amount. The absence, in an oscillation photograph, of spots present in the corresponding rotation photograph gives clues to the crystal symmetry (Ref. 10, p. 60; Ref. 14, p. 114).

The next stage of interpretation is the use of the intensities to locate individual atoms in the unit cell. The amplitude of an x-ray beam scattered by a series of planes with indices *hkl* is proportional to the *structure factor*, $F(hkl)$. Since the intensity, or energy, of an x-ray beam is proportional to the square of the amplitude, the intensity of a spot with indices *hkl* is proportional to the square of the particular structure factor for those indices.

The structure factor includes the effect of scattering from all atoms in the unit cell, and is calculated for a given structure by superimposing the beams from various atoms with suitable phase differences. It is expressed as a sum of terms, one for each of the atoms. One of the forms in which it may be written is:

$$F(hkl) = \sum_i F_i \cos 2\pi \left[\frac{hx_i}{a} + \frac{ky_i}{b} + \frac{lz_i}{c} + \beta_i(hkl) \right] \qquad (3\text{-}9)$$

The index i designates the particular atom for which a term in the sum is being evaluated. The coordinates of the atom in the cell are x_i, y_i, and z_i. F_i is the scattering power of atom i and is taken as proportional to the number of electrons in the atom. The quantities a, b, and c are, as usual, dimensions of the unit cell. The angle β_i is a phase angle which is related to how far atom i is from the point in the unit cell taken as the origin.

For an unknown crystal, a structure is postulated, the structure factor for each reflection of interest is calculated from equation 3-9, and the experimental results are compared with the calculated ones. The structure is revised to reduce discrepancies and the calculation repeated until agreement with the observed intensities is attained (Ref. 3, p. 218; Ref. 10, p. 109).

Not only is this method time-consuming, but it must be started with a reasonable approximation to the correct structure; the latter may be obtained from the experimental data by a *Fourier analysis*. Any quantity which varies periodically can be expressed as the sum of a series of sine or cosine terms, called a Fourier series. The electron density, ρ, varies, as one goes through a crystal, by a pattern which is repeated for each unit cell. Thus it is advantageous to modify our idea of x-ray scattering from that by discrete atomic centers to that by a distribution of electron density over the whole cell.

The one-dimensional variation of the electron density would then be represented by an equation such as:

$$\rho(x) = \sum_{n=-\infty}^{n=+\infty} C_n \cos 2\pi\left(\frac{nx}{a} + \alpha_n\right) \qquad (3\text{-}10)$$

The constant C_n is the coefficient of the nth term and is to be determined. The quantity α_n is the phase angle, fixed by the value of the function at $x = 0$.

In three dimensions, the analogous equation is:

$$\rho(x,y,z) = \sum_h \sum_k \sum_l C_{hkl} \cos 2\pi\left[\frac{hx}{a} + \frac{ky}{b} + \frac{lz}{c} + \alpha(hkl)\right] \qquad (3\text{-}11)$$

Because of the nature of the Fourier analysis, it turns out that the coefficient C_{hkl} for the term with indices hkl is the structure factor for that combination of indices, and this result leads to the equation:

$$\rho(x,y,z) = \frac{1}{U_0} \sum_h \sum_k \sum_l F(hkl) \cos 2\pi\left[\frac{hx}{a} + \frac{ky}{b} + \frac{lz}{c} + \alpha(hkl)\right] \qquad (3\text{-}12)$$

where U_0 is the volume of the unit cell.

Equations 3-9 and 3-12 have a reciprocal relationship to one another. The indices h, k, and l, the reader will recall, were obtained by taking reciprocal distances. Thus we see that summing the structure factor over *reciprocal space* gives the electron density distribution, while summing the electron density over real space in the same way gives the structure factor. Two functions related to one another as are the electron density and the structure factor occur frequently in the study of electromagnetic radiation and are said to be *Fourier transforms* of one another.

Equation 3-12 can now be used to calculate an electron density map of a crystal. Specific values for the coordinates x, y, and z can be inserted and the contributions of all the observed reflections of various *hkl* values can be computed and summed. The detail evident in the resulting map depends on how closely spaced are the points at which calculations are made and how many reflections are observed (Ref. 3, pp. 208, 219). When a map of sufficiently good resolution has been obtained, the places of maximum electron density correspond to the centers of the atoms and thus give the atomic "positions." Fig. 3-16 shows an example in which sections of constant electron density through the three-dimensional map have been plotted.

Such a calculation constitutes a job of tremendous extent; in fact, for a crystal of any complexity, it is only feasible if an electronic computer is available. Accordingly, the calculations are often simplified by making *two-dimensional projections*. These yield the electron density distribution that one might observe by looking along one axis through a transparent unit cell. If one looked in the z direction, for example, the projection could be obtained by evaluating ρ for various values of x and y, using the equation:

$$\rho(x,y) = \sum_{h}\sum_{k} F(hk0) \cos 2\pi \left[\frac{hx}{a} + \frac{ky}{b} + \alpha(hk0) \right] \qquad (3\text{-}13)$$

Of course, one may not be able to see all the atoms in the unit cell in such a projection, for some may be hidden behind others.

To this point, we have neglected one key difficulty in the calculation of ρ. One can not tell from the experimental data what value to use for the phase angle α. This is, indeed, the critical problem in the present state of the science of inter-

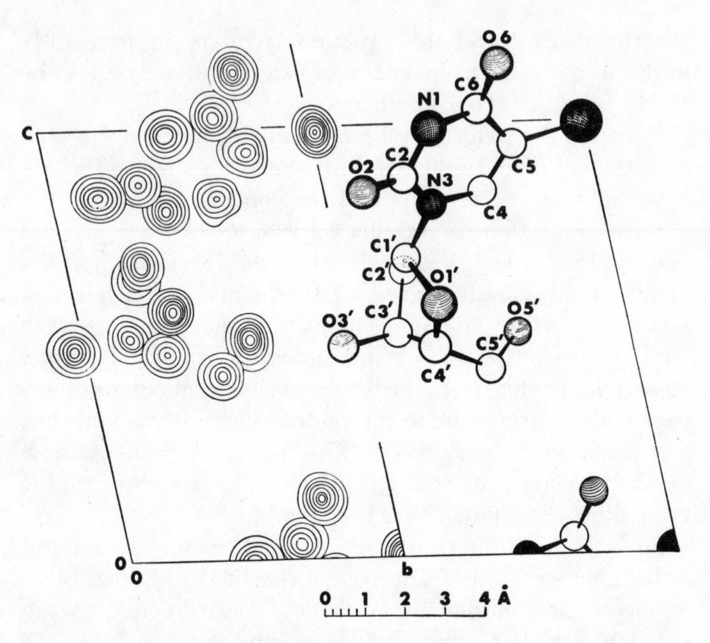

Fig. 3–16. Sections of the three-dimensional electron-density distribution of 5-iododeoxyuridine taken through the atomic centers, and a perspective drawing of the molecule and its location in the x and y directions of the unit cell. Carbon, nitrogen, and oxygen atoms are labeled C, N, and O, respectively. (From N. Camerman and J. Trotter, *Science*, **144,** 1349 (1964).)

pretation of diffraction patterns. It is quite difficult, perhaps, to understand exactly what the nature of this problem is, but a crude explanation can be given. Imagine two cosine waves interfering with one another in a region in space. A given pattern of variation of the resulting amplitude can be generated by an infinite number of different combinations of the amplitude of each of the waves with the phase shift between them; the resultants differ only in the position where the wave maximum occurs. To a device which measures only the intensity of the resultant wave, the position of the wave peak makes no difference. In optical microscopy, it is possible to collect light scattered at the same instant by various parts of a specimen by use of a lens system, and thus obtain what is called *coherent* reflection. But there is no lens available to collect x-rays in the same fashion, and each x-ray diffraction spot is obtained independently from the other spots, so that all relative phase information is lost.

The phase problem usually requires that one resort to a trial and error method. If the positions of the scattering atoms can be assumed, the phase angles are then determined. Equation 3-12 can be used with observed values of $F(hkl)$ and estimates of the phase angle to calculate the electron density function. From the atomic position indicated by this function better phase angle values can be found, and the calculation repeated. If the initial guess as to structure is reasonable, such a process of *refinement* will lead to smaller differences between successive approximations as the calculated structure converges toward the correct one.

Several methods for aiding in solution of the phase problem have been developed. If a heavy atom, such as a metal atom, is present in the unit cell, the reflections from this atom predominate over all the others, and so it forms a natural origin on which to base all calculations (Ref. 3, p. 214). If isomorphous crystals can be obtained, such as a pair differing only in that one has chlorine atoms where the other has bromine atoms, comparison of the reflections of the crystals indicates which are associated with the atom that is different. Still another method is referred to as a *Patterson projection.* If a Fourier sum is taken with the square of the structure factor rather than just $F(hkl)$ itself, the result is a vector map. Information about positions of atoms is lost, but the lengths and directions of all lines joining pairs of atoms in the crystal are obtained, and structures of moderate complexity may then be reconstructed (Ref. 10, pp. 127, 137).

Evaluation of X-Ray Methods. For simple crystals, such as those of the elements, extremely accurate interatomic distances can be obtained, valid to four, five, or sometimes six significant figures. The effect of thermal vibration on interatomic distance is usually quite a bit larger than the experimental error, so that the temperature of the determination becomes important.

One limitation on usefulness is the inability of the method to locate accurately hydrogen atoms. This is a consequence of the low scattering power of the very light atom for x-rays.

For more complex crystals, there is no straightforward method for analyzing the structure. Quite a bit of skill and experience is needed to carry out an analysis. Electronic computers have greatly enhanced the applicability of the method, and a number of researchers are currently automating the diffraction determinations by use of radiation counters and mechanical arrangements which feed data directly to the computer.

For a few materials it has not been possible to establish structures even with considerable work by experts. The approximations used have failed to refine; that is, they do not converge toward an exact solution. This may be the result of something unusual in the structure, such as a difference from cell to cell. It has thus been found in some cases that there are several positions in the unit cell in which a given atom or group may be situated, and that this group is statistically distributed among these positions over the unit cells in the whole crystal. Such a situation can be allowed for in the treatment, but the analyst must realize exactly what is occurring before he can make this allowance.

There is still concern over whether the phase problem will ever be solved in the sense that phase angles can be obtained directly from the data. Certain criteria can be set up for acceptable phase angles, such as the requirement that the electron density nowhere be negative. In a few cases, it has been possible to introduce these criteria directly into the computational process.

Finally, there is the question as to the uniqueness of the structure found. The question always may remain, for a crystal of any degree of complexity: is there some other structure which equally well satisfies the diffraction data? There is not a general way, applicable to all crystals, of answering this question.

Electron Diffraction

Electrons, as well as rays of electromagnetic radiation, have a wave nature, as will be explained in Chapter 5, and can undergo diffraction. We shall consider electron diffraction as it is applied to gases, rather than to condensed phases. Electrons impinging upon atoms are scattered primarily by nuclei rather than by the electrons, which do most of the scattering of x-rays. The scattering probability of an atom for an electron is as much as a million times greater than for an x-ray. As a consequence, a much lower density of matter is appropriate than can be used for x-rays and exposure times in electron diffraction can be relatively short.

In a gas, molecules are tumbling end over end in random fashion. Thus the vectors joining the members of corresponding pairs of atoms, each pair within a different molecule, are uniform only in magnitude and not in direction. Furthermore, the distances between atoms in neighboring molecules are no longer of significance. In other words, the repeat distances within molecules are preserved in the gas, but the other relationships which exist in a crystalline solid are lost. Therefore, fewer parameters are obtainable in electron diffraction; both for this reason, and because of the requirement of sufficient volatility to exist in the gas phase, fairly small molecules are particularly suited for study by this method.

Experimental Procedure. The equipment for electron diffraction consists of a chamber, operated at a relatively high vacuum in order to reduce random or multiple scattering of the electron beam. The source of electrons is a heated filament, and, as they leave this filament, the electrons are accelerated by a positive electrode at a potential of perhaps forty thousand volts. In the center of this positive electrode is an aperture, and electrons passing through this aperture have a velocity corresponding to the kinetic energy resulting from the effect of a potential difference of forty thousand volts acting on the electronic unit of charge. The higher the velocity of the electrons, the shorter their wavelength; the wavelength in angstroms is related to the voltage, V, by the expression, $\lambda = 12.225/\sqrt{V}$. One advantage of electrons compared to x-rays for structural studies is that the wavelength can conveniently be made much shorter. Forty thousand volts corresponds to about 0.06 Å. The shorter wavelength permits observation of a higher number of scattering orders, since one wavelength path difference corresponds to a smaller angular displacement in the diffraction pattern.

The sample to be studied is allowed to leak from a jet into the diffraction chamber, where the electron beam passes through it and then falls upon a photographic plate, on which there is produced a pattern consisting of a number of concentric bands. To a considerable degree, the apparent band structure is an optical illusion, for if a plate exposed in this way is traversed with a microphotometer, an optical device which measures the amount of darkening, the intensity is found to decrease from the center of the plate outward in a stepwise fashion. The eye translates this pattern into alternating dark and light rings.

Interpretation of Results. The data of electron diffraction, then, include the positions of diffraction maxima and their estimated relative intensities. Several types of scattering of electrons contribute to the pattern obtained. Electrons scattered either by electrons of the sample or by single nuclei rather than by pairs of nuclei yield a background which falls off rapidly as the direction of observation moves away from that of the undeflected beam.

The part of the diffracted radiation which carries the structural information, however, is that produced by the effects of two neighboring nuclei; this portion has an intensity which *fluctuates* with increasing deflection angle. It may be described by an expression called the *Wierl* equation:

$$I(\theta) = I_0 K \sum_{i=1}^{N} \sum_{\substack{j=1 \\ i \neq j}}^{N} Z_i Z_j \frac{\sin sr_{ij}}{sr_{ij}} \tag{3-14}$$

I_0 is the intensity of the incident electron beam. K is a scale factor, of which the value need not be known. The quantity s is defined as $(4\pi/\lambda) \sin (\theta/2)$, where λ is the wavelength of the incident beam. The angle θ is the angle of deviation from the path the electrons would take if there were no deflection and the summation is taken over all possible pairs of these atoms. Z is the atomic number, and r_{ij} is the distance between atoms i and j.

The Wierl equation may be used in a trial and error procedure in which the positions and intensities of the maxima are calculated for an assumed structure, the calculated values are compared with the observed pattern, the assumed structure is modified slightly, and the calculation is repeated until what seems to be the best agreement is reached.

An example to illustrate the application of the Wierl equation is the molecule CF_3Cl, which is expected to be approximately tetrahedral in structure. The summation, corresponding to equation 3–14, is:

$$I(s) = 6Z_{Cl} Z_F \frac{\sin sr_{Cl-F}}{sr_{Cl-F}} + 6Z_C Z_F \frac{\sin sr_{C-F}}{r_{C-F}}$$

$$+ 2Z_C Z_{Cl} \frac{\sin sr_{C-Cl}}{sr_{C-Cl}} + 6Z_F{}^2 \frac{\sin sr_{F-F}}{sr_{F-F}} \tag{3-15}$$

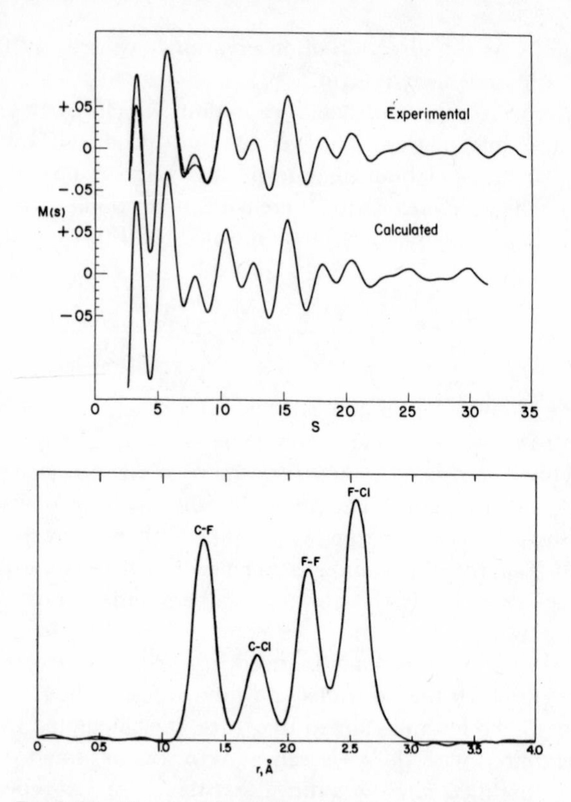

Fig. 3–17. Electron diffraction intensity curves (upper) and radial distribution function (lower) for CF_3Cl. (From L. S. Bartell and L. O. Brockway, *J. Chem. Phys.*, **23**, 1860 (1955).)

The agreement between experimental and calculated curves for the structure chosen as best is shown in Fig. 3-17, taken from the work of Bartell and Brockway.

The Radial Distribution Function. Often it is possible to predict the approximate structure of a molecule by analogy with others. However, the trial and error method may be very tedious and lengthy if the first approximation is a poor one. Fortunately, there is a more direct way of estimating internuclear distances from the experimental data, parallel to Fourier analysis of x-ray diffraction results.

Suppose we modify equation 3-14 to replace the discrete atoms in the molecule by a continuous function which represents the variation of the probability of finding various values of interatomic distances in the molecule, $f(r)$. If this *radial distribution function* is plotted against r, the curve has peaks at values of r corresponding to interatomic distances present in the molecule. The equation now represents an integration over the continuously varying quantity r, rather than a summation over discrete values of r:

$$I(s) = K' \int_{r=0}^{r=\infty} f(r) \frac{\sin sr}{sr} dr \tag{3-16}$$

We can invert this equation by a Fourier transformation, interchanging the two functions I and f, and the two variables r and s.

$$f(r) = K \int_{s=0}^{s=\infty} I(s) \frac{\sin sr}{sr} ds \tag{3-17}$$

From the experimental results, $I(s)$ is known, and so the radial distribution function can be determined. This function for CF_3Cl is shown in Fig. 3-17.

For other molecules there may be a number of interatomic distances with very nearly the same value, which are not well-resolved in the radial distribution function. This is illustrated in Fig. 3-18, for the compound sulfur tetrafluoride.

Examination of the radial distribution curves indicates small ripples superimposed on the genuine peaks or on the base line. These arise in the Fourier inversion which strictly requires, as indicated by equation 3-16, integration of the diffracted intensity out to infinity. Of course, in practice, the intensity can only be estimated out to some finite value of s. The ripples, if they happen to fall near peak maxima,

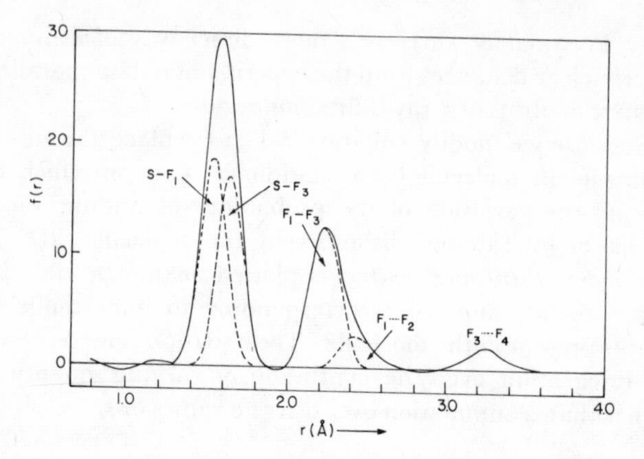

Fig. 3–18. The radial distribution curve for SF_4. The dotted lines show the resolved peaks for individual atom pairs. (From K. Kimura and S. H. Bauer, *J. Chem. Phys.*, **39**, 3174 (1963).)

may distort slightly the true position. The ripples are minimized by introducing a *damping factor*, e^{-as^2}, which reduces the weight given to the intensities at high angles:

$$f(r) = \int_0^{s_{\max}} sI(s)e^{-as^2} \sin sr\, ds \qquad (3\text{-}18)$$

The principal problem in the application of these equations is the proper correction of the observed intensities for the "background" intensity. In 1935, Pauling and Brockway showed that it is possible to obtain reasonably good results by the following procedure: the integral in equation 3-17 is replaced by a sum which has one term for each observed "ring":

$$f(r) = \sum_k I_k \frac{\sin s_k r}{s_k r} \qquad (3\text{-}19)$$

The intensity *estimated by eye* for the *k*th ring is used as I_k; s_k is the value of s corresponding to the angle at which the ring appears. Many of the structural data in the literature have been obtained in this way.

The Sector Method. Recently, instruments have been devised which compensate, in whole or in part, for the background by placing a rotating heart-shaped sector in front of the photographic plate to reduce the time of exposure of the central part of the plate, compared to the exposure time of parts of the plate at higher scattering angle (Ref. 4, p. 430).

The sector does not completely eliminate the effect of background, but it makes it much easier to correct for the remaining background. The plate can be examined by a photometer to obtain a quantitative curve of intensity versus distance from the center. On this curve, a line corresponding to the background can be drawn in by eye. The resulting corrected quantitative intensities are then used with equation 3-18 to give the radial distribution function. If the background curve has been estimated incorrectly, certain regions will have negative values, which make no sense for a probability function, and the background may then be appropriately adjusted to eliminate these.

The Equilibrium Interatomic Distance. One of the important aspects in the interpretation of experimental results regarding molecular geometry is the circumstance that atoms in molecules are undergoing vibrations. Thus a molecule is not a static thing, but a dynamic system. For two bonded atoms, there is a certain interatomic distance, called the equilibrium distance, at which the two atoms would be if there were no vibration. The atoms are sometimes closer together than the equilibrium distance and sometimes farther apart. The displacements of the atoms toward one another are not generally so great, simply because the electron clouds are bumping into one another, as are the distances moved by the atoms when they go apart from one another. Thus, the average bond length is almost invariably greater than the equilibrium bond length. For example, in chloroform, the electron diffraction result for the carbon-chlorine bond distance is 1.783 ± 0.003 Å, but the equilibrium separation is about 0.008 Å less. Furthermore, thermal vibrations may reduce the accuracy of structural analysis by broadening the diffraction peaks.

Evaluation of the Method. Electron diffraction is limited to molecules of a certain size: not only must the sample be sufficently volatile, but the number of molecular parameters which can be obtained is limited by the fact that only perhaps ten to twenty diffraction maxima can be resolved in the pattern. Within this range of applicability, accuracy is

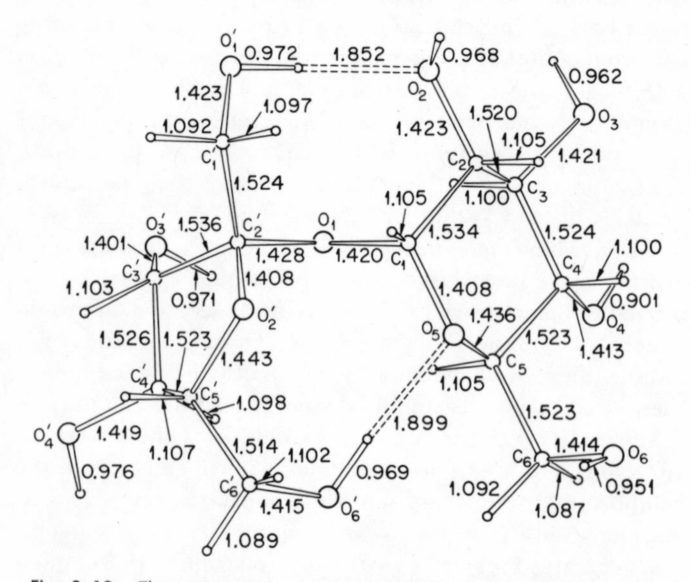

Fig. 3–19. The sucrose molecule, showing highly precise interatomic distances as determined by neutron diffraction. The small circles are hydrogen atoms and the dashed lines indicate hydrogen bonds from the hydroxylic hydrogens to neighboring oxygens. (Private communication, G. M. Brown and H. A. Levy, Oak Ridge National Laboratory; *Science*, **141,** 921 (1963).)

limited primarily by the effects of thermal vibration. An exception to this is the case of hydrogen atoms, which simply have so low a scattering power for electrons that they may be no more than a blur in the electron density pattern. The method shares with x-ray diffraction the problem of uniqueness of the solution found. In fact, the question here is more serious, since there are fewer numbers obtained experimentally per atom to be located.

Neutron Diffraction

In order to locate hydrogen atoms much more satisfactorily than can be done by x-ray or electron diffraction, it is possible to carry out a diffraction experiment with neutrons. The large mass of these particles gives a relatively good probability that they will interact with a hydrogen atom. The limitation of this procedure is that of obtaining a neutron source. A beam of neutrons can be brought out from a nuclear reactor, and thus neutron diffraction work is limited to the vicinity of a reactor which yields a neutron beam of adequate intensity. An example of the results of a structural analysis by this method is shown in Fig. 3-19.

chapter four

ELECTRICAL POLARIZATION IN MOLECULES

WHEN AN electrically neutral molecule is placed in a uniform electric field, there is no net force tending to move the molecule. The field pulls the positive charges in the molecule in one direction and the negative charges in just the opposite direction, and the two forces cancel one another. However, if the molecule has a *dipole moment*, the external field will exert on it a torque, or turning force.

The presence of a permanent dipole moment in a molecule simply means that the average position of the positive charges is toward one end of the molecule, whereas the average position of the electrons is toward the other end. Placed between two electrodes, the molecule will experience a pull of its positive end toward the negative electrode and of its negative end toward the positive electrode.

The magnitude of the torque on a molecule is equal to the strength of the applied electric field multiplied by the dipole moment of the molecule. This statement gives an experimental definition of the magnitude of the moment. The latter is also equal to the total amount of charge of either sign involved in the molecular charge distribution, multiplied by the distance between the centers of the positive and of the negative charge distributions. Experimentally, it is possible to measure only the moment, and, for a given magnitude of the dipole, one can not determine whether there is a large amount of charge separated by a smaller distance or a small amount of charge separated by a larger distance.

An electron and a proton, each of which has a charge of 4.80×10^{-10} electrostatic units, would have a dipole moment of 4.8×10^{-18} esu-cm if separated by a distance of 1 Å (1 Å $= 10^{-8}$ cm). A moment is usually expressed as a multiple of 1×10^{-18} esu-cm, a unit which is called the debye and abbreviated as d.

Moments of Some Simple Molecules

The simplest case of a molecular dipole moment is that of a diatomic molecule. If the two atoms are identical, the molecule has no moment, for the bonding electrons are shared equally, as in N_2, O_2, or Cl_2. If the two atoms are those of different elements, the molecule almost always has a moment, for the electronegativities of the atoms are different and the bonding electrons are unequally shared. Thus in HCl and NO, the chlorine and oxygen atoms, respectively, form the negative ends of the molecules, and the hydrogen and nitrogen atoms form the positive ends.

For a diatomic molecule, the information we can obtain from a measurement of the dipole moment is limited to a qualitative or semiquantitative indication of its bond polarity. For example, the moments of a series of related molecules, such as the hydrogen halides, may be compared to give an idea of the relative ionic character of the bonds (Ref. 11, p. 78).

In a molecule containing three or more atoms, the symmetry may be established by the presence or absence of a dipole moment, and, in some cases, the magnitude of the moment may be used to distinguish between isomers or to estimate the bond angles in a molecule. One attempts always to apply the basic idea that the moment of the molecule is the resultant of adding together contributions from each bond in the molecule, each with its proper direction.

The molecule carbon dioxide has no moment, indicating that the carbon-oxygen bonds are equivalent to one another and oppositely directed. Sulfur dioxide, a formally similar molecule, does have a moment; this could perhaps result from nonequivalence of the two sulfur-oxygen bonds, but experience tells us that electrons move freely enough to cancel out any difference between adjacent bonds joining one atom to several other identical atoms. Accordingly, it is concluded that the sulfur dioxide molecule is nonlinear, and this is confirmed by other methods of investigating its geometry.

Whatever the magnitude of a moment associated with a bond or group, several such groups arranged symmetrically about an axis can produce no component of the resultant dipole moment perpendicular to that axis. Furthermore, there can be no component of the moment perpendicular to a plane of symmetry—a plane such that each atom is mirrored by a like atom on the other side of the plane. All planar molecules, such as ethylene and benzene, are automatically included in this class, for the plane of the molecule is a plane of symmetry.

Further illustrations of molecules with zero moments are boron trichloride and boron trifluoride. Thus they are planar, in contrast to compounds containing nitrogen or phosphorus bonded to three atoms, such as ammonia or phosphine, which have dipole moments. A different sort of symmetry occurs in phosphorus pentafluoride and phosphorus pentachloride, which have zero moment. In these, which have the structure of a trigonal bipyramid, there is a three-fold symmetry axis and a plane of symmetry perpendicular to that axis.

Triphenyl phosphine has a moment of 1.4 debye, and trimethylamine has a moment of 0.86. The reader should find it interesting to try to explain why triphenylamine, in contrast, has a near-zero moment. (It is often necessary to say "near-zero" because experimental uncertainty in determination of a dipole moment is quite large when the moment is small.)

Dipole moments afford a means of distinguishing between isomers of compounds, that is, between different molecules with the same formula which differ in the atomic arrangement and therefore in symmetry properties. For instance, the two possible 1,2-dibromoethylenes are:

Both are planar molecules; the first is the *cis* and the second is the *trans* form. The cis compound has a moment of 1.3 d, while the trans compound has zero moment.

How the Dielectric Constant of a Liquid Is Measured

The usual method of determination of the dipole moment of a material involves measurement of the *dielectric constant* of a gas or liquid containing the substance. Suppose that the space between the plates of an electrical condenser, or capacitor, is filled with a sample of liquid or gas and a potential difference is applied. A certain amount of charge can be built up on the condenser plates for a given voltage, as described in Chapter 2. The ratio of this charge to the charge on the plates when the same voltage is applied to the capacitor without matter between the plates is termed the dielectric constant of the sample.

The dielectric constant of a material is related to the extent to which the material can be *polarized* when it is placed in an electric field. Polarization is the development of charge on the surface of the sample, and for a sample between electrodes, the sign of the charge which is produced on the surface is opposite to the sign of the charge on the electrode adjacent to it. In the presence of polarization, an extra amount of charge equal to the surface charge on the sample can flow to the electrode.

In a sample which is a *dielectric*, that is, one which has by definition no electrical conductivity, polarization can not occur by migration of ions as it can in a conductor; the only mechanism remaining involves the effects of dipoles within molecules. If the molecules of the sample have permanent dipoles and are free to rotate, they are oriented by the electric field: the negative ends turn toward the positive electrode and the positive ends toward the negative electrode. In the interior of the sample, the effects produced by various dipoles cancel one another, but at each surface adjacent to an electrode there is left a net charge.

Whether or not the molecules involved have permanent dipoles, the applied electric field will create dipoles by drawing the electrons in one direction and the positive nuclei in the same molecule in the opposite direction. The result is said to be a dipole *induced* by the field; how the effect of induced dipoles may be separated from that of permanent dipoles will be described later.

Although dielectric measurements have been made on gaseous samples, the concentration of molecules in the gas phase is so low that very sensitive measuring equipment must be used. If the substance is a liquid, determinations cannot be made on the pure material, because the dipoles are now too close together and interact with one another. Consequently the usual procedure is to dissolve the sample in a nonpolar solvent, and then make measurements at various concentrations, which may be extrapolated to infinite dilution.

The cell used for measurements of dielectric constant usually consists of several coaxial cylinders which are the electrodes, mounted in a glass vessel. The capacitance of the empty cell is measured and then the measurement is repeated on the cell containing a solution of the substance under study. After corrections have been made for the capacitance contributions of the leads to the cell, the ratio of the two results is the dielectric constant of the solution.

The capacitance of the dielectric cell may be measured by making it part of the tuned circuit of an electronic oscillator, arranged as described in Chapter 2. The frequency of oscillation is related to the capacitance of the cell plus that of the other elements in the circuit. Usually a substitution method is employed, which utilizes the fact that the capacitance of a system of several elements in parallel is equal to the sum of the capacitances of the individual elements. With the cell containing the sample out of the circuit, a precision condenser with a calibrated dial is used to tune the oscillator to a frequency which is the same as that produced by a crystal-controlled reference oscillator. Identity of frequencies is established by observing the beat note obtained when signals from the two oscillators are mixed together. The frequency of this resultant is equal to the difference between the frequencies of the oscillators and so is zero when the two frequencies are identical. This procedure is called the *heterodyne beat* method.

The sample cell is now placed in parallel with the precision condenser. The amount by which the capacitance of the latter must be reduced to restore the frequency of oscillation of the circuit to that of the reference oscillator is equal to the capacitance added when the cell was placed in the circuit.

Calculation of the Dipole Moment

The equation relating the dielectric constant, ϵ, and the polarization for a single substance is:

$$P_M = \frac{\epsilon - 1}{\epsilon + 2} \frac{M}{d} \tag{4-1}$$

The polarization is here expressed per mole as P_M, with M the molecular weight; d is the density of the substance. In a solution for dipole moment determinations, the solvent usually has no permanent dipoles but it does contribute to the induced polarization. The polarization contributed by the solute is obtained by subtracting the solvent contribution from the total observed. Assuming that the molar polarization of the solution is the weighted average of molar polarizations of the two components leads to the following equation:

$$P_{\text{soln}} = x_1 P_1 + x_2 P_2 = \frac{\epsilon - 1}{\epsilon + 2} \frac{x_1 M_1 + x_2 M_2}{d} \tag{4-2}$$

The subscript 1 refers to the solvent and 2 to the solute; the x's are the respective mole fractions.

Taking P_1 as the molar polarization of the pure solvent, P_2 may be calculated at various concentrations and extrapolated to $x_2 = 0$. In this limit, which corresponds to infinite dilution, the polar molecules are far enough apart so that they do not interact with one another. However, the values of dipole moments obtained in solution differ slightly from those measured in the gas phase because the dipolar molecules induce dipoles in the solvent molecules.

The polarization due to the solute must now be divided into that portion corresponding to the permanent dipoles and that corresponding to the induced dipoles. The total polarization of a substance is often described by the following equation:

$$P_M = \frac{4}{3} \pi \mathcal{N} \left[\alpha + \frac{\mu^2}{3kT} \right] \tag{4-3}$$

The first term gives the contribution of the induced dipoles, which is proportional to the electrical polarizability of the molecules, α. The second term gives the contribution of the permanent dipoles having moment μ. $\mathcal{N}$ is Avogadro's number, k is a constant, known as the Boltzmann constant, and T is the absolute temperature.

That part of polarization contributed by permanent dipoles may be identified by its inverse dependence upon temperature. Thermal motion destroys the orientation of the permanent dipoles in the electric field as collisions buffet the molecules about; this is reflected by the appearance of T in the denominator of the second term of the polarization expression. Thus if P_M is plotted against $1/T$, the slope of the straight line obtained is equal to $4\pi \mathcal{N}\mu^2/9k$. From this slope, the permanent moment may be calculated.

Change of temperature does not affect induced dipoles, since these are always induced in the direction of the field, and, as a molecule turns, the mobility of the electrons allows an induced dipole easily to realign itself to follow the field.

An alternative method of evaluating the induced dipole contribution is to carry out a suitable measurement of polarization under conditions such that the permanent dipoles cannot keep up with a very rapidly alternating electrical field. Interestingly, a suitable alternating field of sufficiently high frequency is that associated with light waves. The contribution of induced dipoles is given by the molar refraction, which is related to the refractive index, n:

$$R_M = \frac{n^2 - 1}{n^2 + 2} \frac{M}{d} \tag{4-4}$$

The refractive index may be measured directly and substituted in equation 4-4 to give the molar refraction, or the molar refraction may be estimated from a knowledge of the atoms and bonds constituting the molecule, since each such unit contributes an amount which varies little from molecule to molecule (Ref. 5, p. 387).

Bond Moments and More Complicated Molecules

In the interpretation of dipole moments of complex molecules, it is often assumed that each bond between a certain combination of atoms makes a contribution to the overall dipole moment which varies only slightly from one molecule to another. On this basis, the moment of a molecule may be predicted from the vector sum of bond moments, or a measured dipole may be interpreted in terms of molecular geometry. Great care must be taken in use of this idea, however, since interactions between bonds and contributions of unshared electrons may modify the bond moments.

The bond moment approach may be conveniently applied to a substituted benzene, since the principal part of the molecule is planar and therefore only two-dimensional. The usual procedure is to take as the bond moment of a group, the dipole moment of the monosubstituted benzene containing that group. This is really the difference between the C-substituent moment and the C—H moment, but the latter cancels out in comparisons. Thus the dipole moment of chlorobenzene is 1.58 d and this is taken as the chlorine substituent moment. Vector addition would predict the same value for metadichlorobenzene, as shown in Fig. 4-1, and the observed value of 1.48 d is in reasonable agreement. For paradichlorobenzene, the observed moment is zero, which is

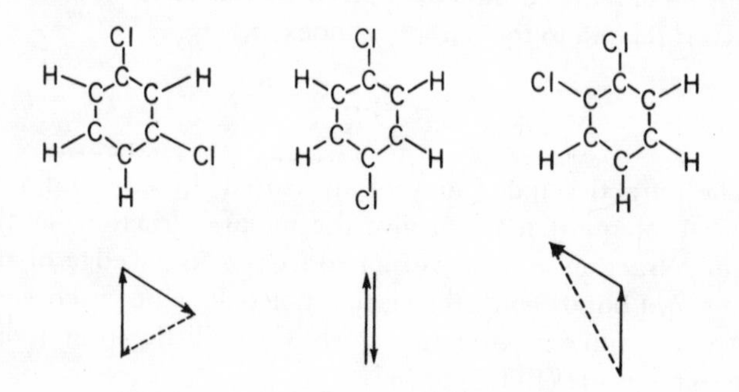

Fig. 4-1. Dipole moments of the dichlorobenzenes. Bond moments are shown as solid lines in the diagrams beneath each formula, and the predicted resultants are shown as dashed lines.

consistent with the direction of the moment being along the C—Cl bond axis. For orthodichlorobenzene, the value is 2.27 d compared to a calculated value of 2.74 d. This relatively large deviation is attributed to a combination of steric repulsions of the two substituents adjacent to one another and the effect of each C—Cl dipole in inducing an opposing dipole in the neighboring C—Cl bond.

In hydroxybenzene, or phenol, the dipole moment in solution is 1.6 d. In paradihydroxybenzene, the moment is not zero, but is 1.4 d. This indicates, of course, that the direction of the moment is not along the C—O axis, but rather at some angle to that axis, so that the groups substituted at opposite positions in the aromatic ring do not have moments directly opposed. The C—O—H bond angle is closer to 90° than to 180°, as shown in Fig. 4-2, and the observed moment

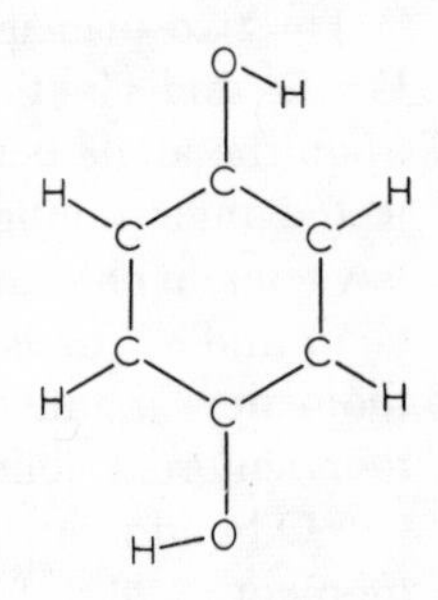

Fig. 4-2. Paradihydroxybenzene, shown with one possible arrangement of the hydroxylic hydrogens, which can rotate about the O–O axis.

is the *average*, over all relative orientations of the two O—H groups, of the resultant of the two moments.

An investigation of the structure α-chlorocyclopentanone illustrates the use of model compounds in the interpretation of dipole moment data.* Either of two forms, shown in Fig. 4-3, might be expected to correspond to the normal state

*Brutcher, Roberts, Barr, and Pearson, *J. Am. Chem. Soc.*, **81,** 4915 (1959).

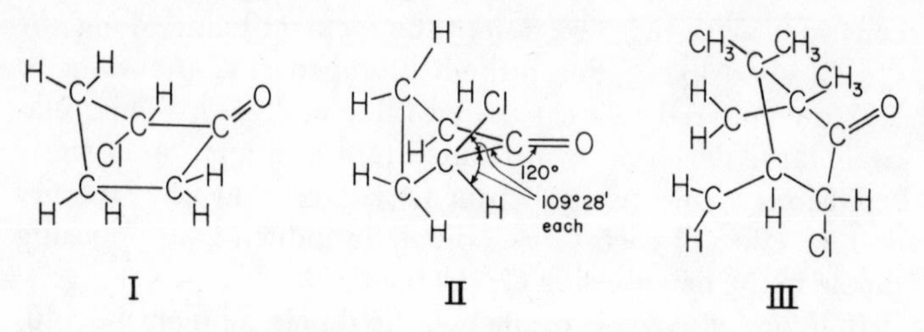

Fig. 4–3. (I and II) Two forms which might be assumed by α-chlorocyclopentanone; (III) the reference compound, α-chlorocamphor.

of the molecule. The *envelope* (I) has four carbon atoms in a plane with the fifth out of plane. The *half-chair* (II) has three adjacent carbons in a plane with the other pair of carbon atoms twisted so that one is as far above the plane as the other is below.

The two principal dipole contributions are those of the C—Cl and C═O bonds. The resultant moment depends upon the angle between these bonds. Estimates of the projected angle (along the axis of the two carbons to which the oxygen and chlorine are attached) are 75° to 80° for the half-chair and 87° to 94° for the envelope form. The C—Cl bond moment was taken as 2.1 d, from the average of values in monochlorocyclohexane and two dichlorocyclohexanes. The C═O bond moment was calculated from the observed dipole moment, 3.98 d, for α-chlorocamphor (III), where the projected angle is approximately 60°. The resulting value, 2.91 d, was then used with the C—Cl moment to calculate the projected angle in α-chlorocyclopentanone, assuming a C—C═O angle of 120° and a Cl—C—C angle of 109°28′. The result was 77°, which agrees quite well with the angle in the half-chair form.

chapter five

QUANTUM THEORY, WAVE MECHANICS, AND THE BOLTZMANN DISTRIBUTION

THE EFFECTS which have been discussed up to this point can be understood and, for the most part, explained by considering the radiation which interacted with matter as consisting of a train of waves. Now, however, the fact that radiation has a dual nature must be taken into account; in certain experiments the radiation behaves as though it were composed of distinct particles rather than being continuous, as waves are usually supposed to be. It is interesting that, in the seventeenth century, Isaac Newton developed a corpuscular theory of light. He attempted to explain refraction of light on passing into matter as the result of an increase in velocity of the particles or corpuscles in matter, and, when later experiments showed the velocity of light to be less in matter than in empty space, the idea of particles of light became discredited. Contemporary with Newton's work, Huyghens, Descartes, and others developed the wave theory, which seemed capable of explaining the refraction and diffraction of light quite satisfactorily. As a result, the wave theory was accepted until very near the end of the nineteenth century, when a number of phenomena were found with which it was inconsistent.

Max Planck, in an effort to derive a suitable formula which would fit the experimental results on the wave length distribution of radiation emitted by a heated solid, proposed in 1901 what became the basis for the quantum theory. His proposition was equivalent to the assumption that an oscillating system, such as a molecule, must be, at any one time, in one of a series of discrete energy levels. We can visualize these allowed levels as forming a ladder of energies, as shown in Fig. 5-1. A corollary may then be drawn that the radia-

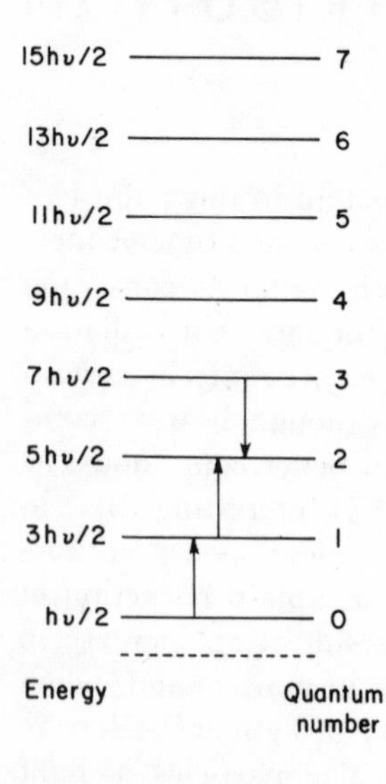

Fig. 5-1. Energy states of an idealized vibrating molecular system. Integers on the right denote the number of quanta of energy possessed by the system in excess of the energy of the lowest state. The arrows show examples of spectroscopic transitions which may occur in some molecules as far infrared radiation is absorbed or emitted.

tion emitted from a molecule as it changes from one level to another must carry a definite amount of energy, and must come as a pulse as the molecule "jumps" from the initial level to the final level, rather than as a continuous wave.

The emphasis by Planck was upon the discrete or "quantized" nature of the energy states in which the material system can exist; Einstein extended this idea to include a particle nature for radiation itself. When a ray of ultraviolet or visible light strikes a suitable metal surface, it causes electrons to be ejected from the surface, a phenomenon utilized in many photoelectric cells and called the *photoelectric effect*. The detailed nature of the photoelectric effect was shown by Einstein to be explainable if the light falling on the metal surface is not a continuous wave extending over all the surface, but rather a series of photons "peppering" the surface; thus, over a very short interval of time, all of the energy which the ray brings to the surface goes to the vicinity of one atom on the surface as a photon lands there.

The quantum theory is the basis for two important quantitative relations which we shall use. The first states that the amount of energy, E, carried by one photon is proportional to the frequency of the photon, ν:

$$E = h\nu \tag{5-1}$$

The constant of proportionality, h, is known as Planck's constant and has the numerical value 6.6×10^{-27} when the energy is in ergs and the frequency is in reciprocal seconds. In accord with this relationship, the energy carried by an x-ray quantum is quite large, so that an x-ray photon can cause a change requiring a large amount of energy, such as the ionization of an atom or the breaking of a chemical bond. A photon of ultraviolet light has somewhat less energy but may still be able to create ions or to break weak bonds; often it will, on striking an atom or molecule, merely excite an electron into a different orbit. A photon of infrared radiation is relatively weak in energy and may not be able to produce any electronic change in a molecule, but only perhaps a change in the mechanical motions of the molecule.

A second quantum principle describes the allowed states

of a molecular system. Verbally it may be stated: *the angular momentum is quantized in units of $h/2\pi$.* Once more Planck's constant, h, appears. To explain this statement, let us begin with the general meaning of momentum. A moving body, having a mass m and a velocity v, can be stopped by a certain force acting for some length of time. The product of the required force and the time it must act is equal to the product of the mass and the velocity, mv, and is called the momentum of the body.

Angular momentum about an axis describes the corresponding requirement to stop the rotation of a body about that axis. The magnitude of the angular momentum is mvr, where m is the mass which is moving, v is its linear velocity, and r is the distance the mass is away from the axis. The expression is like that for linear momentum but includes an additional "lever-arm" factor, r. The linear velocity may be replaced by the angular velocity, ω, times the radius r, yielding $m\omega r^2$. Angular momentum is a quantity which has both magnitude *and* direction. The direction is uniquely defined as that of the axis about which the rotation is occurring, and the angular momentum of a body is often represented by a vector directed along this axis and with a length proportional to the magnitude of the angular momentum.

The quantization of angular momentum means that its magnitude may be described in terms of a *quantum number*, J, which may be either an integer, such as 0, 1, 2, and so on, or a half integer, such as 1/2, 3/2, or 5/2. *Experimental results* at first indicated that the allowed values of angular momentum were equal to $J(h/2\pi)$. Later development of wave mechanical *theory*, taking into account the wave nature of material particles, showed that the values are given by $\sqrt{J(J+1)}\,(h/2\pi)$.

There is no real contradiction between experiment and theory, however. $J(h/2\pi)$ is, in fact, the largest value of the angular momentum which can be measured by most experiments, for these are performed so that they measure the maximum value of the angular momentum about an axis which has the direction of an applied electrical or magnetic field. If the axis of rotation of the molecule coincided with this field direction, the *uncertainty principle* would be violated, for both the energy and position of the spinning system would be exactly defined. Thus, the rotational axis is always tilted away from the direction of the external field, and the "true" magnitude of the angular momentum is $\sqrt{J(J+1)}$ $(h/2\pi)$, although this amount is not measured. When J is very large, the maximum measurable value approaches the true value.

The quantization of angular momentum was introduced as a postulate to explain certain experimental results, with moderate success over the period from about 1900 to 1920. However, it began to be realized in the early 1920's that matter has associated with it a wave nature, and this was confirmed by carrying out electron diffraction experiments, somewhat like those described in Chapter 3, using metallic crystals as the "diffraction gratings." Shortly after this, Schrödinger, de Broglie and others showed that, by making certain postulates about the wave nature of matter, it was possible to deduce both the detailed nature of the quantization of angular momentum and the magnitude of the equivalent wave length, $\lambda = h/mv$, of electrons and other particles from a unified set of principles. The essence of these is embodied in Schrödinger's differential equation. The solutions of this equation are so-called "wave-functions" that describe the behavior in space and time of matter waves.

The wave mechanics of Schrödinger cannot be deduced from more basic principles or rigorously proved; its acceptance depends upon the fact that so many varied phenomena can be described quantitatively by making deductions from a small set of basic postulates. We shall discuss in this book molecular energy levels, or stationary states, and the transitions which molecules undergo from one state to another by absorption or emission of appropriate amounts of energy. The energies of these states and the rules which govern the probability of changes from one state to another are intimately related to the mathematics of wave mechanics.

Another important principle which will be employed in the discussion of energy levels of molecules is known as the Boltzmann distribution law. It states that, when a collection of molecules is at thermal equilibrium, the ratio of the number of molecules in state 2, having energy E_2, to those in state 1, having energy E_1, is given by the quantity

$$\frac{\text{Molecules}_2}{\text{Molecules}_1} = \frac{P_2}{P_1} e^{-(E_2-E_1)/RT} \tag{5-2}$$

The quantities P_i represent what are sometimes called statistical weights. They describe how many different ways the molecules may have the quantity of energy E_i. To help visualize what P represents, we may take as illustration an example from atomic structure. An atom has only one 2*s* orbital but it has three 2*p* orbitals; if there is only one electron to be placed in 2*p* orbitals, the energy is the same regardless of which of the three contains the electron, and thus the occupation of a 2*p* orbital by a single electron has a statistical weight of three, compared to one for a 2*s* orbital.

The chemist commonly deals with three types of molecular energies which are important in determination of molecular geometry and electronic structure. These are the energies of rotation of molecules as a whole, the energies of vibration of atoms within a molecule, and the energies of excitation of electrons to higher-energy molecular orbitals. Fortunately, the radiation which is emitted or absorbed when transitions occur in one of these three categories is usually well separated in frequency from that for the others. Table 5-1 summarizes the principal divisions of molecular spectro-

TABLE 5-1. Regions of Molecular Spectra

Energy Type	Spectral Range	Magnitude of Energy Change, kcal/mole
Rotation	Far infrared and microwave	10^{-4}–10^{-1}
Vibration	Near infrared	10^{-1}–10^{1}
Electronic orbital	Visible and ultraviolet	10^{1}–10^{2}

scopy. In the next two chapters we shall deal with molecular rotations and vibrations; the scope of this book does not permit discussion of electronic transitions, which are not as directly applicable to the task of "measuring molecules."

chapter six

ROTATIONAL SPECTRA OF MOLECULES

ONE OF the types of energy which a molecule in the gas phase may possess is that associated with rotation about its center of mass. Atomic masses move during molecular rotation and the energy of rotation is simply the kinetic energy of these moving masses. This energy is calculated by multiplying the mass of each atom m by the square of the velocity of the atom, dividing by 2, and summing the results over all the atoms in the molecule. In the resulting summation equation, the subscript i is the label for a particular atom:

$$E = \sum_i \tfrac{1}{2} m_i v_i^2 \qquad (6\text{-}1)$$

Practically, the mass of an atom may be considered as concentrated at the nucleus, since the electronic masses are negligibly small. As a result, rotation of a monatomic molecule, such as an atom of one of the inert gases, moves no mass and thus involves no kinetic energy; likewise, linear molecules have no kinetic energy for rotation about the long axis of the molecule.

Moment of Inertia

Any rotational motion of a body may be resolved into rotation about three principal axes, which are mutually perpendicular to one another and which intersect at the center of gravity of the object. The axis of highest symmetry (an axis such that rotation about it brings the atomic framework into identical positions more often than once every 360°), if there is one, is always one of the principal axes.

The characteristics of rotation about an axis are determined by the distribution of mass of the body projected into a plane perpendicular to the axis. Suppose, then, we look along one of the principal rotational axes in the molecule 1,2-dichloroethylene, which is shown in Fig. 6-1. There

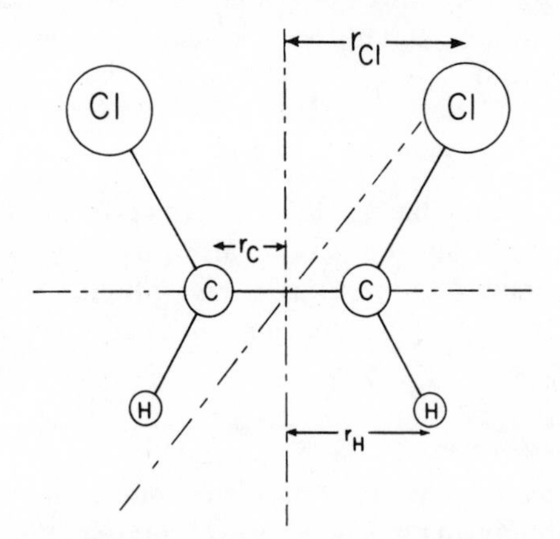

Fig. 6–1. *Cis*-1,2-Dichloroethylene, showing the principal axes and the distances of the atoms from one of these axes.

are two carbon atoms of mass m_C, two hydrogen atoms of mass m_H, and two chlorine atoms of mass m_{Cl}. These are located at distances r_C, r_H, and r_{Cl}, respectively, from the chosen axis of rotation. The linear velocity with which any of the masses, m_i, moves as the molecule rotates about this axis is equal to the angular velocity, ω, in radians per second, times the distance from the axis, r_i. Under the assumption that the molecule is rigid, that is, that the interatomic distances and bond angles are fixed, the angular velocity is the same for all the atoms in the molecule. We can then write the equation for the kinetic energy:

$$E_{rot} = 2(\tfrac{1}{2}m_C\omega^2 r_C^2) + 2(\tfrac{1}{2}m_H\omega^2 r_H^2) + 2(\tfrac{1}{2}m_{Cl}\omega^2 r_{Cl}^2)$$

$$= \frac{\omega^2}{2}\sum_i m_i r_i^2 \qquad (6\text{-}2)$$

Now the usual kinetic energy expression, for rectilinear motion, is $\tfrac{1}{2}mv^2$. Equation 6-2 can be converted into the same form by defining a quantity, I, called the *moment of inertia*, as $\sum_i m_i r_i^2$, so that:

$$E_{rot} = \tfrac{1}{2}I\omega^2 \qquad (6\text{-}3)$$

A molecule may have a different value of the moment of inertia for rotation about each arbitrary axis. However, when the moment of inertia is given without specific definition, what is referred to is the moment about one of the three principal axes.

Allowed Energy Levels

Macroscopic bodies may have any rotational velocity and correspondingly any kinetic energy of rotation, but, for molecules, the allowed values are restricted according to the principle that angular momentum is quantized in units of $h/2\pi$, as described in Chapter 5.

For a molecule containing several atoms, the angular momentum, P_{rot}, is given by a summation over the atoms:

$$P_{rot} = \sum_i m_i \omega r_i^2 = \omega \sum_i m_i r_i^2 = I\omega \qquad (6\text{-}4)$$

Quantum restrictions limit the angular momentum to the values given by $\sqrt{J(J+1)}\,(h/2\pi)$, where J is a quantum number which may have zero or positive integral values. For calculation of the corresponding rotational energies, the square of the angular momentum, $I^2 \omega^2$, or $J(J + 1)h^2/4\pi^2$, is substituted in equation 6-3:

$$E_{\text{rot}} = \tfrac{1}{2}I\omega^2 = \frac{I^2\omega^2}{2I} = \frac{J(J+1)h^2}{8\pi^2 I} \qquad (6\text{-}5)$$

The energies available to the rigid rotator are thus seen to be proportional to the product $J(J + 1)$, where J may have the values 0, 1, 2, 3, 4, and so on. Fig. 6-2 shows the appearance of the lower portion of the energy level diagram, which, of course, has no definite upper limit.

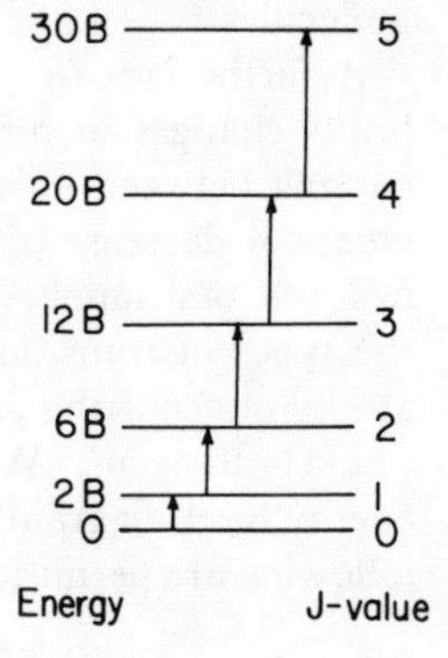

Fig. 6–2. Rotational energy levels of a diatomic molecule. The arrows show some transitions which might occur in an absorption spectrum. Capital B is the rotational constant defined on page 86.

Linear Molecules

The equations we have just developed apply to one degree of freedom of rotation—rotation about a single axis—which can be characterized by a single value of the moment of inertia and by one series of values of the quantum number J. This is very nearly the situation in linear molecules, such as carbon dioxide or acetylene or any diatomic molecule. Here the moment of inertia about the molecular axis is zero, and the two moments of inertia about the other two principal axes, perpendicular to the molecular axis, are identical. Thus only one numerical value of I occurs for a given molecule, and the energy is defined by only one quantum number.

Radiation interacts with a molecule to produce rotational transitions *only if the molecule has a dipole moment.* The electric dipole in the molecule provides a "handle" by which the fluctuating electric field of the radiation can exert a torque on the molecule. Molecules without dipole moments are normally rotating and can undergo transitions in rotational levels; however, these transitions are produced by processes we may term "mechanical," such as collisions with other molecules.

A further restriction governing spectroscopic transitions limits changes in rotational quantum number to those occurring between adjacent energy levels: that is, J may increase or decrease by one unit only. This statement is one example of a number of *spectral selection rules* which describe the types of transitions that have a reasonably great probability of occurring as contrasted with those which are very unlikely to occur. When this selection rule is applied to the energy level diagram, it is seen that transitions such as the following are permitted:

$J = 0$	to	$J = 1$	2 units of energy
$J = 1$	to	$J = 2$	4 units of energy
$J = 2$	to	$J = 3$	6 units of energy
$J = 3$	to	$J = 4$	8 units of energy

Thus the allowed transitions form a regular series: since frequency is proportional to energy difference, the difference in frequency between any two successive members of the series is the same as the frequency of the first member. The "unit of energy" referred to in the table above is $h^2/8\pi^2 I$. If we divide this by h, we obtain an expression for what is often termed the *rotational constant* and is given the symbol B:

$$B = h/8\pi^2 I \tag{6-6}$$

The frequency of a rotational transition is given by $2B$ multiplied by the J value of the *upper* state involved.

There results for a linear molecule a series of spectral lines, as represented in Fig. 6-3. For light diatomic molecules, such as HF, the rotational spectrum falls in the far infrared region, but for heavier molecules with correspondingly larger moments of inertia, the spectrum is in the microwave region (Ref. 7). Good rotational spectra, characteristic of individual molecules, can only be obtained in the gas phase, for in condensed phases molecular collisions and intermolecular interactions broaden the energy levels until they overlap.

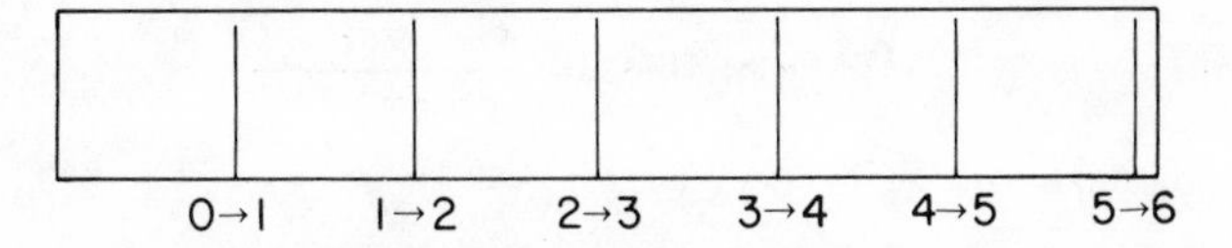

Fig. 6-3. Rotational spectrum of a diatomic molecule. The numbers indicate the initial and final levels of each transition. The left-hand end of the diagram corresponds to the zero of energy.

We may suppose that, if a molecule along with the electrical dipole it carries is rotating at some frequency, the radiation which could accelerate the molecular rotation would be required to have the same frequency. This is qualitatively borne out by the spectrum observed, for the higher the J value for the initial level from which a transition is to occur, and thus the greater the frequency of molecular rotation, the larger the energy of the transition, and therefore the higher the frequency of the radiation which will induce the transition.

For a diatomic molecule, the moment of inertia can be expressed quite simply as:

$$I = \frac{m_1 m_2}{m_1 + m_2} r_{12}^2 \qquad (6\text{-}7)$$

where m_1 and m_2 are the masses of the two atoms and r_{12} is the distance between them. If a rotational spectrum can be obtained for the molecule, the rotational constant B is found from the separation between lines, which is equal to $2B$, and the moment of inertia can be calculated from B. The interatomic distance, r_{12}, can then be obtained by equation 6-7 from I and the known values of the atomic masses.

As an example, consider the molecule carbon monoxide, composed of C^{12} and O^{16}. The line corresponding to the $J = 0$ to $J = 1$ transition is at 115,271 megacycles per second, which corresponds to a value of B of 1.93 cm^{-1}. By equation 6-6:

$$1.93(3.00 \times 10^{10}) = \frac{6.62 \times 10^{-27}}{8\pi^2 I}$$

$$I = 14.48 \times 10^{-40}\ g\text{-}cm^2$$

By equation 6-7, this corresponds to a value of 1.13×10^{-8} cm for the interatomic distance.

Until this point, we have disregarded the dependence of interatomic distance on the speed of rotation. As a molecule is excited to higher rotational levels and its angular momentum increases, the centrifugal force pulling against the binding force of the bond increases. Thus rotation stretches the molecule, increasing both r and the moment of inertia. This reduces somewhat the energy of rotation for a given value of J, and the allowed energies are now given by the equation:

$$E_{rot} = B_0 hJ(J+1) - DhJ^2(J+1)^2 \qquad (6\text{-}8)$$

The quantity D is the *centrifugal distortion constant*; the stronger the bond, the smaller its value. B_0 is the value of the rotational constant appropriate to the *ground* rotational state, so that the value of I calculated from B_0 applies to the ground state.

When the energy difference for the spectral transition from state J to state $J + 1$ is derived from equation 6-8, the following expression results:

$$\Delta E = 2B_0h(J + 1) - 4Dh(J + 1)^3 \qquad (6\text{-}9)$$

In the interpretation of a spectrum, the parameters B_0 and D are adjusted until the best numerical fit to the experimental results is obtained for frequencies calculated from this equation. This procedure is particularly important when the series of lines obtained does not include those for low values of J, either because the intensity is too low or because they fall in an inconvenient portion of the spectrum. Then the equation may be used to extrapolate the observations so as to obtain the rotational constant for the ground state. The latter may be found to five or six significant figures, since microwave frequencies can be measured very accurately. For example, an accurate determination of B_0 for the carbon monoxide molecule discussed above yielded 1.93124 cm^{-1}. The calculation of interatomic distances is, in fact, limited in accuracy by the accuracy with which atomic masses are known.

A triatomic linear molecule has two independent interatomic distances to be determined:

$$m_1 \overset{r_{12}}{\longleftrightarrow} m_2 \overset{r_{23}}{\longleftrightarrow} m_3$$

An infinite number of combinations of r_{12} and r_{23} will fit the one moment of inertia which can be obtained from the rotational spectrum; thus, the values of the two distances cannot be directly calculated. However, if one substitutes for one of the atoms in the molecule another isotope, one will have a molecule with unaltered distances and only the masses changed (because of the effects of vibration, this statement is not strictly correct, but the situation will be explained in the next chapter). By determining the rotational spectra of both molecules, equations for the two moments of inertia in terms of the known masses and two unknown distances may be solved simultaneously. The great accuracy of frequency measurements in microwave spectroscopy allows a reasonable number of significant figures to appear in the final result despite the loss of significant figures which occurs in solving the simultaneous equations.

Data for four isotopic modifications of HCN serve to illustrate the way in which molecular dimensions may be obtained by the method of *isotopic substitution*:

Molecule	$H^1C^{12}N^{14}$	$H^2C^{12}N^{14}$	$H^1C^{13}N^{14}$	$H^2C^{13}N^{14}$
B_0, Cps $\times 10^{-6}$	44,316.0	36,207.5	43,170.1	35,587.6

The substitution of deuterium for hydrogen is seen to have a larger effect on the moment of inertia than the substitution of C^{13} for C^{12}, and thus should give more accurate values of the interatomic distances. However, any two of these molecular species may be used in the calculation of these distances. The reader may wish to carry out the calculation for this molecule and compare his results with the literature values of 1.064 Å for the C—H bond distance and 1.156 Å for the C—N bond distance.

The Stark Effect

From the wave equation for a rotating molecule, it is found that the states of the molecule are described by the quantum number for total angular momentum, J, which we have already used, and by a second quantum number, M_J, which can have integral values from $-J$ through zero to $+J$. Accordingly there are $2J + 1$ different states for each value of J, but these all have the same energy if the molecule is isolated. However, when the molecule is placed in an external electrical or magnetic field, the angular momentum becomes quantized with respect to the field, and the states with different values of M_J may have different energies. The projection of the angular momentum vector in the field direc-

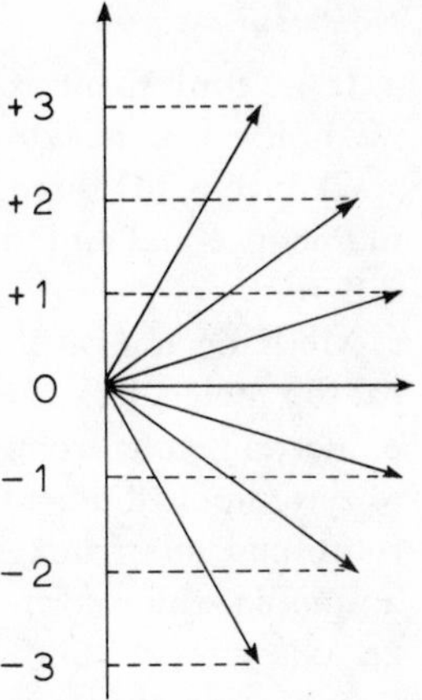

Fig. 6–4. Possible orientations of an angular momentum vector with respect to an applied field in the vertical direction for a spin quantum number, J, of 3.

tion for a state described by M_J is $M_J(h/2\pi)$, as illustrated for $J = 3$ in Fig. 6-4.

Of particular interest in molecular spectroscopy is the *Stark effect*, obtained when a rotational spectrum is observed while the sample is in an electric field. The energy of a dipolar molecule in an electric field depends on the magnitude of M_J, although not on its sign, and there are $J + 1$ different energies for each value of J. Thus the electric field "splits" energy levels and transitions may be observed at different frequencies.

The magnitude of the Stark effect shift in the frequency of a transition from the normal value depends upon the strength of the electric field and upon the dipole moment of the molecule, and may be used to measure the dipole moment. The relative spacings and intensities of the components into which a transition is split permit assignment of the transition to a particular pair of rotational levels, an assignment which is often difficult, particularly in the complex pattern for an asymmetric top molecule to be described below (Ref. 7, p. 164).

Nonlinear Molecules

It is convenient to classify a nonlinear molecule as a *spherical top*, a *symmetric top*, or an *asymmetric top*. These have, respectively, all three moments of inertia equal, two of the moments equal and the third different, or all three moments different.

Methane and carbon tetrachloride are examples of spherical top molecules. Usually the equality of the three moments of inertia results from molecular symmetry, which also leads to zero dipole moment, so that these molecules have no pure rotational spectrum. Examples of the symmetric top are ammonia, chloroform, and benzene; any molecule which has an axis of three-fold or higher symmetry is necessarily at least a symmetric top. Most polyatomic molecules are asymmetric tops.

The total rotational energy for a molecule is given by the equation:

$$E_{\text{rot}} = \frac{P_A^2}{2I_A} + \frac{P_B^2}{2I_B} + \frac{P_C^2}{2I_C} \qquad (6\text{-}10)$$

When the moments of inertia are replaced by the rotational constants A, B, and C, equal respectively to $h/8\pi^2 I_A$, $h/8\pi^2 I_B$, and $h/8\pi^2 I_C$, this becomes:

$$E_{\text{rot}} = \frac{4\pi^2 P_A^2}{h} A + \frac{4\pi^2 P_B^2}{h} B + \frac{4\pi^2 P_C^2}{h} C \qquad (6\text{-}11)$$

For a symmetric top or a spherical top, this equation is simplified by making two or three of the rotational constants equal.

The Symmetric Top. In this type of molecule, the moment of inertia which has the unique value is usually designated I_A, so that $I_B = I_C$. The axis about which I_A is taken is a symmetry axis of the molecule, called the *figure axis*. The total angular momentum is given by the equation:

$$P^2 = P_A^2 + P_B^2 + P_C^2 \qquad (6\text{-}12)$$

The total angular momentum is quantized, with a magnitude related to the value of the quantum number J; accordingly:

$$P^2 = \frac{J(J+1)h^2}{4\pi^2} \tag{6-13}$$

It is found that the component of the angular momentum along the figure axis is also quantized, with a quantum number K:

$$P_A^2 = \frac{K^2h^2}{4\pi^2} \tag{6-14}$$

Since P_A, a component of P, cannot be larger than P, K cannot be larger than J. The values which K can have are thus $0, \pm 1, \pm 2, \pm 3, \ldots, \pm J$.

The last three equations may be combined:

$$P_B^2 + P_C^2 = P^2 - P_A^2 = J(J+1)h^2/4\pi^2 - K^2h^2/4\pi^2 \tag{6-15}$$

This result is now substituted into equation 6-10:

$$\begin{aligned} E_{\text{rot}} &= \frac{P_A^2}{2I_A} + \frac{(P_B^2 + P_C^2)}{2I_B} \\ &= \frac{K^2h^2}{8\pi^2 I_A} + \frac{[J(J+1)h^2/4\pi^2 - K^2h^2/4\pi^2]}{2I_B} \end{aligned} \tag{6-16}$$

Rearranging this equation and introducing the rotational constants A and B as defined above, one obtains the energies of the allowed levels in wave numbers:

$$\tilde{\nu} = BJ(J+1) + (A - B)K^2 \tag{6-17}$$

The dipole moment of a symmetric top molecule lies along the figure axis. The quantum number K describes the angular momentum vector component along this axis, which means that it describes rotational motion occurring in the plane *perpendicular* to the axis, and therefore also perpendicular to the dipole moment. Consequently radiation cannot bring about changes in K. The selection rules are, accordingly, $\Delta K = 0$, $\Delta J = 0, \pm 1$. The absorption wave numbers are then given by $\tilde{\nu} = 2B(J + 1)\ \text{cm}^{-1}$, and the spectrum is, to a quite good approximation, like that of a linear molecule. Furthermore, only B, and therefore only I_B, can be evaluated from the spectrum.

The Asymmetric Top. An asymmetric top molecule almost invariably has a dipole moment. The rotational spectrum is usually rich in lines, and correspondingly difficult to unravel. The total angular momentum is quantized, but no component of it is quantized, so that only the quantum number J is available to characterize the angular momentum of rotational states. For each value of J, there are $2J + 1$ sublevels, which, even in the absence of an external field, have different energies.

The sublevels of each value of J are sometimes labeled by using an index, τ, which varies by integers from $-J$ to $+J$, in order from lowest to highest energy. Thus for $J = 2$, the five levels are designated 2_{-2}, 2_{-1}, 2_0, 2_{+1}, and 2_{+2}. An alternate convention is the use as a double subscript of the K values that the level would have in two hypothetical related symmetric tops obtained by letting I_B in the asymmetric top first become smaller until it is equal to I_C and then letting it grow larger until it is equal to I_A. Both conventions are illustrated in the energy level diagram (Fig. 6-5).

It is possible to derive expressions for the rotational energies of the various levels of an asymmetric top in terms of the three rotational constants. Some of these, for lower values of J, are listed in Table 6-1. In Table 6-2 are given the frequencies of the microwave transitions observed for the *gauche* form of the molecule of normal propyl chloride, CH_3CH_2-CH_2Cl, containing the isotope Cl^{35}. The reader should use these data with the expressions of Table 6-1 to calculate the rotational constants A, B, and C for this molecule, which were found to be 11,829.2, 3,322.6, and 2,853.1 megacycles per second, respectively.

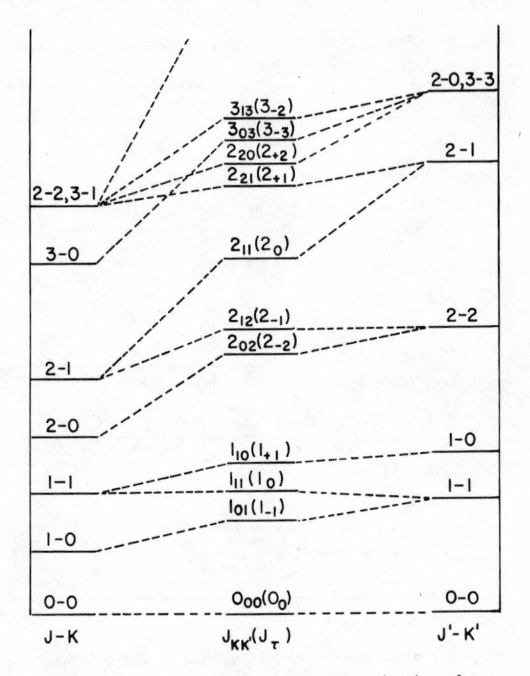

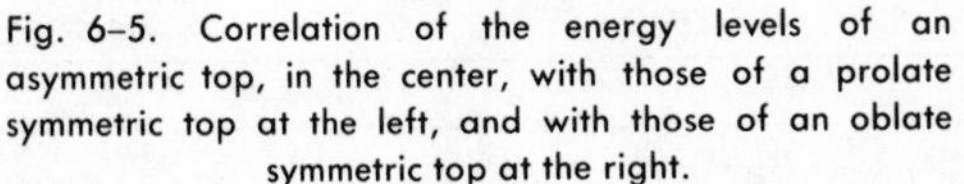
Fig. 6–5. Correlation of the energy levels of an asymmetric top, in the center, with those of a prolate symmetric top at the left, and with those of an oblate symmetric top at the right.

The substance normal propyl chloride is interesting because its molecules exist in the gas phase in two different conformations of nearly equal energy. They may be described by the relative orientations of the methyl group and the chlorine atom about the carbon-carbon bond between the two CH_2 groups. In the *trans* form, these two groups have a projected angle of 180° from one another, while in the *gauche* form, the projected angle between them is 60°. A separate microwave spectrum for each of the two forms is observed, and each part of this spectrum is doubled by the

TABLE 6-1. Energy Expressions for Rotational Levels of an Asymmetric Top Molecule

Level	*Energy*
0_{00}	0
1_{10}	$A + B$
1_{11}	$A + C$
1_{01}	$B + C$
2_{20}	$2A + 2B + 2C + 2\sqrt{(B - C)^2 + (A - C)(A - B)}$
2_{21}	$4A + B + C$
2_{11}	$A + 4B + C$
2_{12}	$A + B + 4C$
2_{02}	$2A + 2B + 2C - 2\sqrt{(B - C)^2 + (A - C)(A - B)}$
3_{30}	$5A + 5B + 2C + 2\sqrt{4(A - B)^2 + (A - C)(B - C)}$
3_{31}	$5A + 2B + 5C + 2\sqrt{4(A - C)^2 - (A - B)(B - C)}$
3_{21}	$2A + 5B + 5C + 2\sqrt{4(B - C)^2 + (A - B)(A - C)}$
3_{22}	$4A + 4B + 4C$
3_{12}	$5A + 5B + 2C - 2\sqrt{4(A - B)^2 + (A - C)(B - C)}$
3_{13}	$5A + 2B + 5C - 2\sqrt{4(A - C)^2 - (A - B)(B - C)}$
3_{03}	$2A + 5B + 5C - 2\sqrt{4(B - C)^2 + (A - B)(A - C)}$

TABLE 6-2. Frequencies of Microwave Spectral Lines for $CH_3CH_2CH_2Cl^{35}$

Transition	*Frequency, Mc/sec*
$0_{00}-1_{11}$	14,682.93
$1_{01}-2_{12}$	20,388.94
$1_{11}-2_{12}$	11,881.80
$1_{10}-2_{11}$	12,820.80
$2_{11}-3_{12}$	19,218.84
$2_{02}-3_{03}$	18,450.95
$2_{12}-3_{13}$	17,810.83

From T. N. Sarachman, *J. Chem. Phys.*, **39**, 469 (1963).

presence of molecules having Cl^{37} along with those having Cl^{35}. Although the *gauche* form is an asymmetric top, the *trans* form is only slightly distorted from a symmetric top, since in it the heavy atoms fall very nearly in a line.

Evaluation of Microwave Spectroscopy

One of the great advantages of spectroscopy in the microwave region is the high degree of accuracy with which transition frequencies may be measured. A disadvantage in locating atoms in molecules is that a maximum of three independent parameters may be evaluated for a molecule of given isotopic composition. The usefulness of the method then depends upon the availability of isotopically substituted molecules in sufficient variety to suit the complexity of the molecule to be studied. Some degree of volatility is required for satisfactory results, but a recent development in technique has been operation of the spectrometer at elevated temperatures as an aid in overcoming this limitation.

chapter seven

MOLECULAR VIBRATIONS

ATOMS WITHIN molecules vibrate about their average positions, undergoing periodic displacements from these positions. Vibration of an atom with respect to other atoms in a molecule involves bending or stretching of the valence bonds which hold it; the bonds may be pictured as flexible springs which tend to restore the atom to its equilibrium position.

Molecular vibrations are quite similar to the vibrations which might be set up in an arrangement of balls connected together by coil springs, if the balls were given an initial impulse and then left to themselves. However, vibrations in the ball-spring system die out fairly quickly because their energy is dissipated in working against friction, while molecular vibrations are frictionless and persist indefinitely in an isolated molecule.

For a monatomic gas, no vibration is possible, since the molecule is completely described by giving the position coordinates. For a diatomic molecule, one kind of vibration is possible—the elongation and contraction of the bond between the two atoms. For more complex molecules, numerous kinds of vibrations occur.

Absorption bands in an infrared spectrum of a substance are usually produced by transitions between vibrational levels. Infrared spectroscopy has become an indispensable tool in the qualitative determination of molecular structure for the preparative chemist. In addition, as we shall see below, information about molecular parameters may be obtained by this method under certain circumstances. For experimental details of infrared spectroscopy, the reader may consult Chapters 3 and 4 of reference 2.

The Harmonic Oscillator

A vibrating molecule can be described by analogy with a vibrating macroscopic system which is called in mechanics a harmonic oscillator. This system obeys Hooke's law: the force tending to restore the system to equilibrium is, at any stage in the oscillation, proportional to the distance from equilibrium, Δx:

$$\text{Force} = -k(\Delta x) \tag{7-1}$$

The coefficient k is a measure of the "stiffness" of the system. The negative sign appears because the restoring force is always directed towards the equilibrium position, while the displacement is measured away from equilibrium.

Suppose a mass is suspended by a spring which obeys Hooke's law. If the mass is displaced vertically and then released, it moves up and down in a cyclic fashion. When the mass is above the rest point, gravity predominates over the spring force. Indeed, the downward pull causes the mass to accelerate downward and pass through the rest point with considerable kinetic energy; the inertia of the mass then carries it past the rest point until all of the kinetic energy has been converted into potential energy of extension of the spring. The mass thus stops and the pull of the spring, which predominates over gravity whenever the body is below the equilibrium point, starts it moving upward. The mass once again reaches maximum velocity and maximum kinetic energy as it passes the rest point. It is carried on by inertia, reaching an upper extreme when it has lost its kinetic energy, and turning downward to begin the whole cycle once again.

The frequency, ν, of a harmonic oscillator is related to the force constant, k, and the mass, m, of the moving object by the equation:

$$\nu = \frac{1}{2\pi}\sqrt{\frac{k}{m}} \qquad (7\text{-}2)$$

Diatomic Molecules

Turning now to the diatomic molecule as an oscillator, we find that its vibrations are approximately harmonic, for the valence bond acts as a good Hooke's law spring so long as it is not stretched or compressed too drastically. Since both atoms are moving, the displacement from equilibrium is the amount by which the internuclear distance exceeds the equilibrium distance, and in place of m in equation 7-2 there is used the effective or "reduced" mass of the system of two bodies, equal to $m_1 m_2/(m_1 + m_2)$, where m_1 and m_2 are the individual masses of the two atoms.

Vibrations on a molecular scale are limited by quantum restrictions. The energies of the possible quantized vibrational states of a harmonic oscillator are:

$$E_n = (n + \tfrac{1}{2})h\nu \qquad (7\text{-}3)$$

The quantum number n is zero or a positive integer, corresponding to states as shown in Fig. 5-1. Any states with vibrational energies between the values given by this expression cannot exist.

Equation 7-3 describes an energy "ladder" with all rungs equally spaced. On this ladder, the various levels all correspond to the *same* frequency of vibration, ν; when the molecule has more vibrational energy, the atoms do move faster, but they simply go farther away from the equilibrium positions at the extremes of the cycle.

For a perfectly harmonic molecular oscillator the spectroscopic selection rule for vibrational transitions states that the quantum number n can change by only one unit. Therefore, the change in energy is always equal to $h\nu$, where ν is the vibrational frequency, and, to a first approximation, all allowed transitions for a diatomic molecule give rise only to a single spectroscopic band. Furthermore, since the energy of a photon of radiation of frequency ν is equal to $h\nu$, the frequency of vibration of the molecule and the frequency of the radiation which can excite it are identical.

Now molecular vibrations can exist in any sort of molecule. They are produced, for example, by mechanical effects when two molecules collide. However, spectroscopic transitions, in which a photon is absorbed or emitted by the molecule, can only occur for a *diatomic molecule* if the molecule has a dipole moment. Consequently, none of the molecules, N_2, O_2, H_2, or Cl_2, has a vibrational spectrum. A general rule, for molecules of any degree of complexity, of which this one for diatomic molecules is a special case, will be given later.

No molecular oscillator is, in fact, perfectly harmonic. As the atoms approach closely to one another, unshared electrons cause the two atoms to repel one another; smaller orbital overlap causes the bond to be weaker when the atoms are far apart. Thus the law of force deviates from Hooke's law. In Fig. 7-1, the curve represents the approximate limits of the vibrations of various energies. The results of anharmonicity are that the energy levels are not quite uniformly spaced, and the selection rule does not hold exactly, so that jumps of two steps become possible, although they are still less likely than one-step transitions. In the spectrum, the two-step transitions appear as *overtones* for which the frequencies are almost, but not quite, twice the frequency of the fundamental.

Vibrations in More Complex Molecules

For molecules which contain more than two atoms, much more complex distortions from the equilibrium configuration can occur. These may include changes in the angles between

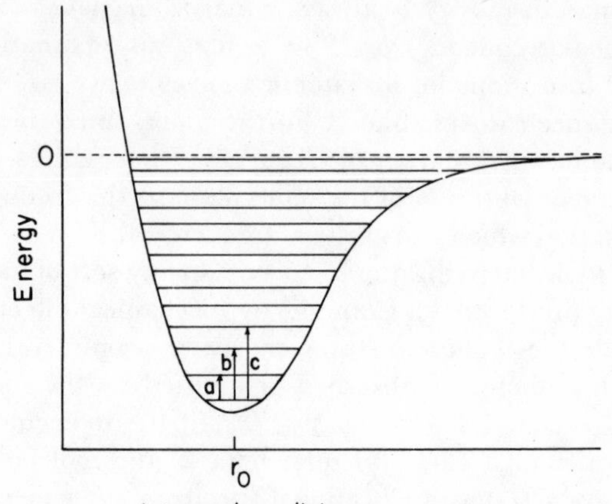

Fig. 7–1. A typical potential energy curve for a real oscillator. The minimum in the curve at distance r_0 corresponds to the equilibrium distance between the atoms. Horizontal lines represent vibrational levels. The deviation from equal spacing between these levels is much exaggerated. Transitions *a*, *b*, and *c* are the fundamental, first overtone, and second overtone, respectively.

interatomic bonds, as well as in the distance between atoms. Some progress in describing these distortions may be made by using the principle that any periodic motion of a molecule, no matter how complicated it may be, can be described as the sum of contributions from each of the members of a basic set of vibrations for that molecule, termed *normal modes of vibration.* There is some weighted average of the normal vibrations which is equivalent to any arbitrary motion.

The number of normal modes for a molecule can be evaluated in the following way. The description of a molecule in terms of the location of each of N atoms requires $3N$ coordinates. However, we usually use three of the coordinates to locate the center of gravity of the molecule, and the positions of the atoms are referred to this center of gravity. Further, we choose molecular axes, two for a linear molecule and three for a nonlinear molecule, and use this number of coordinates to describe the angles which these axes make with an external reference system. The remaining coordinates ($3N - 5$ of them for a linear molecule, or $3N - 6$ of them for a nonlinear molecule) must be available to describe changes in shape of the molecule.

For a diatomic molecule, the value of $3N - 5$ corresponds to the one possible vibration. For a nonlinear, triatomic molecule, there are nine coordinates in all, and six are used in locating the molecule and describing its orientation. Since three coordinates remain, there are three normal modes of vibration, and the nature of these, determined by a mathematical analysis, is represented in Fig. 7-2. The arrows

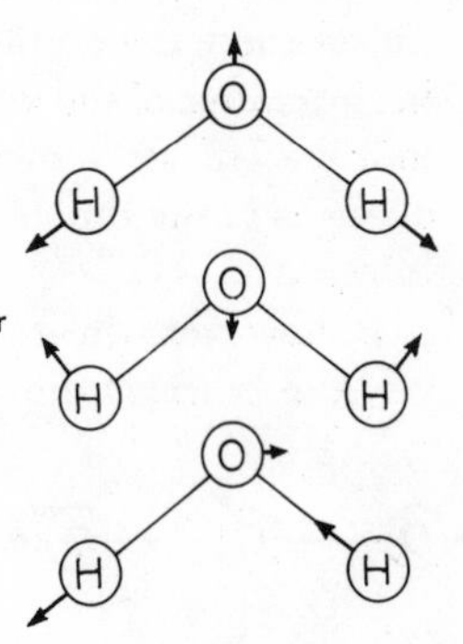

Fig. 7–2. The three normal modes of vibration for water, a nonlinear, triatomic molecule.

represent the displacements of atoms in one half of the vibrational cycle. During the other half of the cycle, the displacements are all in the directions opposite to those of the arrows. The relative lengths of the arrows depend upon the masses of the three atoms.

In addition to the requirement that a set of normal vibrations be just adequate to describe any complex vibration, there are other conditions which are met by the normal modes. The motions are in straight lines, and, in a given normal mode, all of the atoms are vibrating with the same frequency and in phase with one another. This means that all of them reach one extreme of the vibration simultaneously and then reverse direction, going back through the equilibrium positions together and reaching the other extreme of the vibration at the same time. For the majority of molecular types, a complete mathematical analysis of the mechanical problem is necessary to ascertain the nature of the normal modes (Ref. 1, ch. 6).

One aspect of molecular structure about which determination of vibrational spectra may give very significant information is the symmetry of a molecule. For this purpose it is necessary to apply the rule that a vibration will not be represented by a spectral absorption band in the infrared region unless there is a change in the dipole moment of the molecule in the course of the vibration. Of the vibrations shown above in Fig. 7-2 for a nonlinear, triatomic molecule, all cause changes in the dipole moment and are therefore active in the infrared.

If, however, the molecule is linear, like CO_2, the normal vibrations are as shown in Fig. 7-3. Three normal modes are

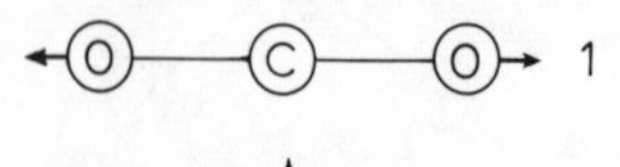

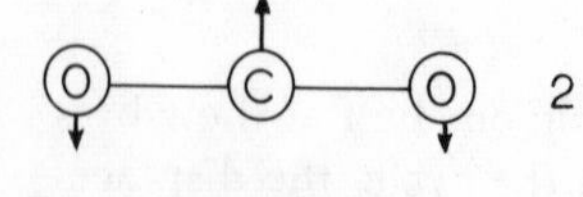

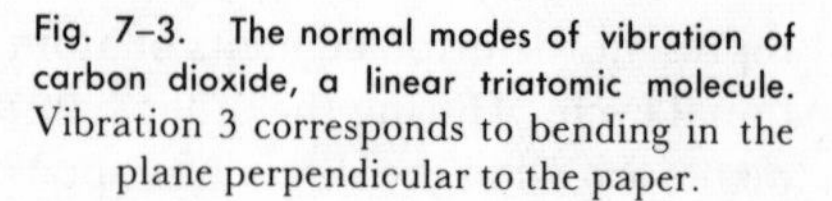
Fig. 7–3. The normal modes of vibration of carbon dioxide, a linear triatomic molecule. Vibration 3 corresponds to bending in the plane perpendicular to the paper.

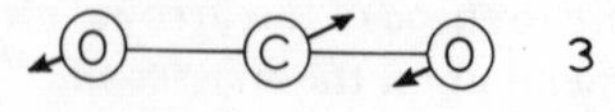

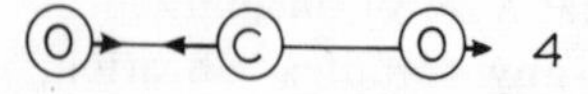

active in the infrared. During the vibration numbered *1* in Fig. 7-3, the symmetrical stretching vibration, the dipole moment of the molecule remains zero. This vibration, therefore, can not be excited by infrared radiation. Vibrations *2* and *3* are identical except for the planes in which the atoms move, and are called a *degenerate* pair of modes, which simply means that their energy is the same. They give rise to only one spectral absorption band. The vibration marked *4* is also active, so that CO_2 has two fundamental absorption frequencies in the infrared, compared to three for nonlinear molecules.

The molecule of boron trifluoride, BF_3, has all four atoms situated in one plane, with the three fluorines symmetrically placed about the boron. A molecule such as NH_3 or NF_3 has the three like atoms at the corners of an equilateral triangle, but the fourth atom is not in the same plane as these three. The planar structure has only three fundamental vibrations which are active in the infrared, while the nonplanar molecule has four; thus the two molecular types can be distinguished by their infrared spectra.

Rotational Structure in Vibrational Bands

Quantitative information about molecular dimensions, aside from qualitative considerations relating to symmetry, cannot be obtained from the frequency of a pure vibrational transition. However, changes in vibrational state are usually accompanied by changes in rotational state. The magnitude of a rotational energy change is smaller than that of a vibrational transition; consequently, the spectrum of any vibrational change consists of a series of lines which are fairly close together, each line corresponding to a different combination of rotational states in the initial and final vibrational state.

If the rotational fine structure can be resolved, rotational constants of the molecule can be evaluated. The precision available varies greatly from molecule to molecule, but there is one case which is of practical importance, even if the precision is low: molecules, such as methane, which have no dipole moment and therefore no pure rotational spectrum do show rotational fine structure in any vibrational transitions which are active.

In Fig. 7-4 are shown "ideal" rotational sublevels for two different vibrational levels, assuming that the moment of inertia of the molecule is not affected by vibration. The sequence of rotational levels in each vibrational state is that described in Chapter 6, where transitions within the same vibrational state were considered. The selection rule which describes allowed transitions is the same here as for pure rotational transitions: $\Delta J = \pm 1$. For many, but not all, vibrations, $\Delta J = 0$ is also allowed.

Because the spectral bands are almost always observed in absorption, we shall consider only vibrational transitions from lower to higher energy. If the rotational transition is also from lower to higher energy, the total energy required is greater than that for the pure vibrational change. A series of lines which constitutes the high frequency part of the band corresponds to this type of change and is called the *R* branch. If the rotational transition is from higher to lower energy, the total energy is less than that for the pure vibrational change; the series of lines in the low-frequency portion of the band is termed the *P* branch. If pure vibrational transitions are allowed, as they are for all vibrations except those in which the atoms move parallel to the dipole moment of the molecule, they form the *Q* branch, a sharp absorption at the center of the band. Thus the *P*, *Q*, and *R* branches correspond to $\Delta J = -1, 0,$ and $+1$, respectively.

Examples of the transitions leading to the structure of vibrational bands are shown in Fig. 7-4. It will be seen that, assuming B independent of vibration, the separations between successive lines in either the *P* or *R* branch are equal to $2B$ cm^{-1}. In the gas phase, the individual lines can often

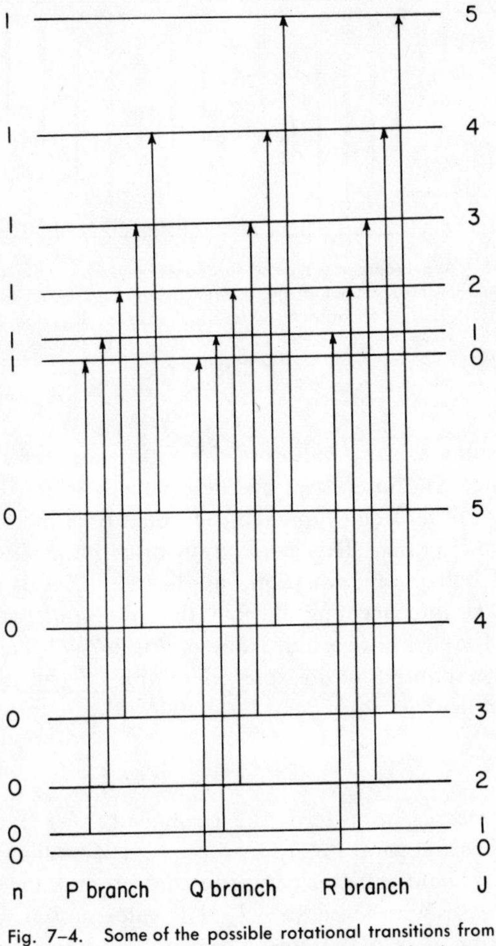

Fig. 7–4. Some of the possible rotational transitions from one vibrational level to a higher vibrational level.

be resolved and B, the rotational constant, can then be evaluated.

If we examine each branch of a band, as illustrated in Fig. 7-5, we observe the intensity rising to a maximum and then

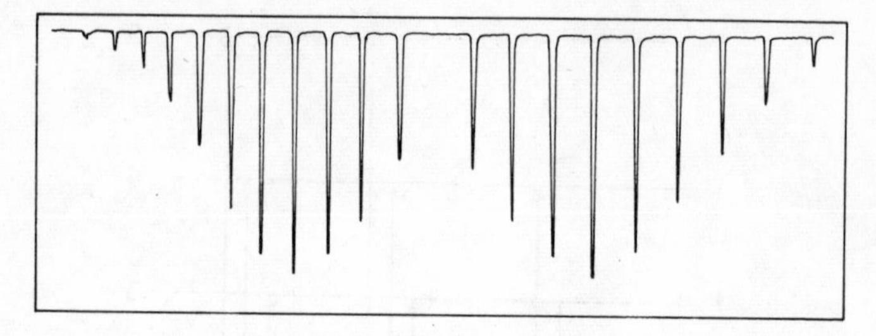

Fig. 7–5. Appearance of a typical vibrational band for a gaseous diatomic molecule, showing resolution of the vibrational structure. The lines on the left constitute the R branch, extending in the direction of higher frequency; those on the right form the P branch, in the direction of lower frequency.

diminishing as the J values of the rotational states involved increase. The intensities are determined primarily by the numbers of molecules in each rotational level in the ground vibrational state. This population distribution is governed by the Boltzmann equation; application of this equation must take into account the fact that the statistical weight for the level with a certain value of J is $2J + 1$, corresponding to the number of possible orientations J can take in an external field:

$$N_J = N_0 (2J + 1) e^{-\frac{J(J+1)h^2}{8\pi^2 IkT}} \tag{7-4}$$

As J increases from zero, the coefficient $2J + 1$ first predominates and causes N_J to increase. At some magnitude of J, the exponential factor begins to control, and, beyond this, N_J decreases with increasing J. The value of J at which the population is a maximum increases with increasing temperature and varies with the moment of inertia of the molecule. The transitions involving the ground state level having this value of J yield the most intense lines in the band. Even if the individual lines cannot be resolved, as is almost always the case for liquid phase spectra because of smearing of energy levels by intermolecular collisions, the distance, $\Delta\tilde{\nu}$, between the maxima in the P and R branches can be measured, and the rotational constant B can be estimated from the equation:

$$\Delta\tilde{\nu} = \sqrt{\frac{8BkT}{hc}} \tag{7-5}$$

It turns out in practice that the variation of B with vibrational state, which we have neglected up to this point, is appreciable. The reason is that the vibrations are not quite symmetric, and thus the average internuclear distance and the moment of inertia are both increased with increasing extent of vibration. Consequently, the separation between rotational levels is smaller in higher vibrational states. The magnitude of the energy decrease is greater in the higher rotational levels, and therefore the transitions in the R branch move closer together and the transitions in the P branch spread apart as the J values concerned increase—in other words, as one moves out from the center of the band to the wings.

It is convenient to represent the rotational constant for the nth vibrational state as B_n, and it is usually well reproduced by the equation:

$$B_n = B_e - \alpha(n + \tfrac{1}{2}) \tag{7-6}$$

in which α is an empirical constant for each molecule. The constant B_e applies to a hypothetical molecular state in which there is no vibration. Since there is some vibration even in the ground state, B_0 will depend upon the asymmetry of the vibration. This is rather important when isotopic substitution is used to obtain moments of inertia as described in Chapter 6, because the vibrational energy for a given vibrational quantum number depends on the mass of the isotope present. Thus, the assumption of independence of bond length and isotopic composition holds quite well for the equilibrium distances deduced from B_e, but not for those in the ground state described by B_0.

chapter eight

SUMMARY AND EXAMPLES

IN THE previous seven chapters, we have examined certain of the physical methods available for establishing qualitatively and quantitatively the geometry of molecules. Other methods of quite extensive applicability have been omitted or barely mentioned: nuclear magnetic resonance, Raman spectroscopy, electronic spectroscopy, mass spectrometry.

As we approach the study of a new molecule, it is usually necessary to use all available methods which are appropriate to its particular characteristics to establish its structure. Some of the considerations which lead to the choice of methods are the physical form in which the material may be obtained, for certain techniques are suitable only for the gaseous state and others only for the solid state, the presence of a dipole moment in the molecule, which is a prerequisite for certain types of spectroscopy, and the size of the molecule, for electron diffraction and spectroscopic methods are limited in the number of independent parameters which can be found for one molecule. By carefully cross-checking the results of several methods and letting one method build on the information obtained from others, the most satisfactory picture of molecular structure is obtained.

What are the present capabilities of structure determination? For many molecules, techniques are rapidly approaching the limit of meaningful accuracy as set by the thermal vibrations of the atoms themselves. A beautiful illustration of the accuracy obtainable in crystal structure analysis by neutron diffraction is that in Fig. 3-19, where bond distances not involving hydrogen are known to an accuracy of 0.002 Å or better and bond distances involving hydrogen to 0.005 Å or better. Of course, results of this precision are probably applicable to the sucrose molecule only in the crystal; in aqueous solution, some of the bond distances involving hydrogen, and perhaps other distances, would be slightly different. Moreover, sucrose is a particularly favorable example: its chemical formula is well-known and it forms nice single crystals.

Occasional molecules are recalcitrant; results obtained by different methods are contradictory or only of low accuracy. Certain sorts of information we would very much like to have seem difficult to obtain. For example, in olefins, is the H—C—H bond angle exactly 120°? In aniline, which has an amino group attached to a benzene ring, are the C—N—H bond angles exactly 120° and is the equilibrium position of the hydrogen atoms precisely in the plane of the ring? Perhaps by the time you read this book, these questions will have been answered; if so, others will have taken their place.

In conclusion, we suggest to the reader a number of interesting examples which he may follow back through the literature, so that he may better understand how problems arise and are resolved. For each molecule, we cite one or two publications, which in turn give references to earlier work.

Sulfur Monofluoride, S_2F_2: R. L. Kuczkowski, *J. Am. Chem. Soc.*, **86,** 3617 (1964).

Dinitrogen Tetroxide, N_2O_4: R. N. Weiner and E. R. Nixson, *J. Chem. Phys.*, **26,** 906 (1957); G. M. Begun and W. H. Fletcher, *J. Mol. Spectroscopy*, **4,** 388 (1960).

Methane and Deuteromethane, CH_4 and CD_4: L. S. Bartell, K. Kuchitsu, and R. J. deNeui, *J. Chem. Phys.*, **35,** 1211 (1961).

Difluoroethylenes, $CFH{=}CFH$ and $CH_2{=}CF_2$: V. W. Laurie and D. T. Pence, *J. Chem. Phys.*, **38,** 2693 (1963).

Ethylmagnesium Bromide, $CH_3CH_2MgBr \cdot 2(CH_3CH_2)_2O$: L. J. Guggenberger and R. E. Rundle, *J. Am. Chem. Soc.*, **86,** 5344 (1964).

Difluorodiazine, N_2F_2: R. L. Kuczkowski and E. B. Wilson, Jr., *J. Chem. Phys.*, **39,** 1030 (1963).

Borazine, $B_3N_3H_6$, and derivatives: E. K. Mellon, Jr., and J. J. Lagowski, *Inorg. Chem.*, **3,** 1694 (1964).

Bromine Pentafluoride, BrF_5: R. S. McDowell and L. B. Asprey, *J. Chem. Phys.*, **37,** 165 (1962).

Formaldoxime, $CH_2{=}NOH$: I. N. Levine, *J. Chem. Phys.*, **38,** 2326 (1963).

REFERENCES AND READINGS

1. Barrow, G. M., *Introduction to Molecular Spectroscopy*, McGraw-Hill, New York, 1962.
2. Bauman, R. P., *Absorption Spectroscopy*, Wiley, New York, 1962.
3. Brand, J. C. D., and Speakman, J. C., *Molecular Structure*, Edward Arnold, London, 1960.
4. Braude, E. A., and Nachod, F. C., eds., *Determination of Organic Structures by Physical Methods*, Academic Press, New York, 1955.
5. Brey, W. S., *Principles of Physical Chemistry*, Appleton-Century-Crofts, New York, 1958.
6. Bunn, C. W., *Chemical Crystallography*, 2nd ed., Oxford University Press, 1961.
7. Gordy, W. Smith, W. V., and Trambarulo, R. F., *Microwave Spectroscopy*, Wiley, New York, 1953.
8. Lonsdale, K., *Crystals and X-Rays*, Van Nostrand, New York, 1949.
9. Moore, W. J., *Physical Chemistry*, 3rd ed., Prentice-Hall, Englewood Cliffs, N. J., 1962.
10. Robertson, J. M., *Organic Crystals and Molecules*, Cornell University Press, Ithaca, 1953.
11. Ryschkewitsch, G. E., *Chemical Bonding and the Geometry of Molecules*, Reinhold, New York, 1963.
12. Sisler, H. H., *Electronic Structure, Properties, and the Periodic Table*, Reinhold, New York, 1963.
13. Weissberger, A., ed., Physical Methods of Organic Chemistry, 3rd ed. (Vol. I of *Technique of Organic Chemistry*), Interscience, New York–London, 1959–60.
14. Wheatley, P. J., *Molecular Structure*, Oxford University Press, 1959.

INDEX